FIRES of MARL

DESIGN
STEVEN BROWN, STEPHEN CRANE,
GREG FARSHTEY, MIRANDA HORNER,
BILL OLMESDAHL, DANIEL SCOTT PALTER,
PETER SCHWEIGHOFER, ED STARK

ADDITIONAL MATERIAL
NIGEL FINDLEY, GEORGE STRAYTON

DEVELOPMENT AND EDITING
GREG FARSHTEY, GEORGE STRAYTON

COVER DESIGN & GRAPHICS
TIM BOBKO

COVER ILLUSTRATION
LISSANNE LAKE

INTERIOR ILLUSTRATIONS
TIM BOBKO,
JAMIE LOMBARDO & RON HILL,
TOM ONEILL, MIKE VILARDI

Publisher: **Daniel Scott Palter** • Associate Publisher/Treasurer: **Denise Palter**
Associate Publisher: **Richard Hawran** • Senior Editor: **Greg Farshtey**
Editors: **Peter Schweighofer, Bill Smith, Paul Sudlow, George Strayton, Eric Trautmann**
Art Director: **Stephen Crane** • Graphic Artists: **Tim Bobko, Tom ONeill, Brian Schomburg**
Sales Manager: **Jeff Kent** • Licensing Manager: **Ron Seiden** • Warehouse Manager: **Ed Hill**
Accounting: **Karen Bayly, Wendy Lord** • Billing: **Amy Giacobbe**

WEST END GAMES • RR 3 BOX 2345 • HONESDALE, PA

D1410655

CONTENTS

INTRODUCTION

Legends.

Every place, every culture has them, even the rough and tumble world of *Bloodshadows*. Whether they're modern and homegrown — like the tales that spring up about that two-timing alchemist down the street and what he poured down his wife one day — or they come slouching out of the distant past, the days of the First Godwar, they can grab hold of your imagination like nothing else. Some might be intriguing, like stories of hidden treasure ... or they can be bait to lure you to what's waiting where the treasure was supposed to be. They'll fill you with hope and they'll fill you with fear, and every emotion in between.

And that's what this book is about.

Within this volume, you'll find the legends of Marl as seen through the eyes of over a half dozen authors. From closer looks at a few of the world's cities to mini-adventures and even short fiction, this book takes you under the skin of Marl and shows you some of the things waiting within.

Ready, pal? Then let's begin ...

LEGEND IN YOUR OWN MIND

First question you're probably asking is, "How do I use this book?" That's an easy one — the source material here is loaded with potential adventures, new enemies for the player characters, and new items for them to seek. Virtually all of the city settings have been detailed elsewhere as well, so you can attach the legends in here to fully fleshed out locations. Wherever your characters might be in the established world of Marl, you can find a legend here to hang an adventure on.

But what if these are not enough? What if you want to build your own legend? How do you go about thinking one up? Here are some guidelines you can use:

1) Why do the player characters care? A legend has to be of some relevance to the characters, something that can affect their lives or that they can affect. It does no good to weave a legend for Padarr if your characters are in Galitia and have no way to get there and take advantage of it. Actually being able to investigate or profit from the legend is essential to its being of some use in your campaign.

2) What's in it for them? Most characters in *Bloodshadows* are not noted for altruism. The fact that there's a legendary ravening Unnatural offing people in the Taxim Quarter probably won't be enough to get them involved — there's going to have to be some perceived profit for them. Maybe there's something of value in that abandoned tenement the resurrected Unnatural is calling home (cash hidden by the mobster that used to own the place, say?), or maybe someone is willing to pay to get this threat to local property values taken down.

Of course, there could be other motivations as well. Maybe one of the characters is suspected of the murders (the local sentinels don't buy the legend of an Unnatural who comes back after every few decades to kill a dozen people or so). Maybe one of the characters' friends or lovers was one of the victims of the killer. Anything that will give them a compelling reason to get involved is okay.

3) Legends, old and new. A Marl legend could date back as far as the Godwar, and that certainly gives you an excuse not to provide the players with many details (since events from those days are so hazy in most history tomes or oral tradition). But the tale could also be of more recent vintage. Feel free to look through citybooks like *Galitia* or *Padarr* and find events or individuals from those cities' pasts that can be used as the basis for legends (for example, Galitia was founded by two generals who distrusted and kept secrets from each other — could there perhaps be some spoils of war still hidden somewhere in the oldest sections of the city?

By the same token, perhaps Arle's mob has begun rubbing out members of a rival gang using a type of magic no one's ever seen before. Can the player characters trace it down and uncover the secret of this new power?)

4) Above all, make it interesting. If all your legends wind up being, "Kill the monster, get the treasure," you're doing something wrong. Remember that legends can have more than one layer, and there's no reason on Marl you have to tell the characters everything. Maybe there is a treasure — but they're going to have to go through a hell of a lot more than one Unnatural to get it. Maybe they'll have to pass through a gate into a whole different dimension. Maybe the treasure won't seem like very much at first glance, but it actually holds a power that could benefit the characters … or destroy them. In this way, the adventure doesn't have to end when they obtain the item — finding out just what it is and what makes it so valuable could be a thread running through your campaign for some time to come.

THIS VOLUME

This book is intended as a supplement for *The World of Bloodshadows*, and you will need the WorldBook and the *MasterBook* to play. The supplements *Galitia, Padarr, Mean Streets*, and the novel *Blood of Tarrian* can also be helpful, but are by no means necessary for enjoyment of this book.

CHAPTER ONE

SELASTOS: THE DOOM CLOCK

Gather 'round fast, little ragamuffins, quick, before the stroke of noon, and hear old Haldemus tell the story of how the Doom Clock came to Selastos Council Hall.

Many years ago, when the city was quickly growing under the rich weight of gold, a dying old literary eccentric from Galitia, Bartholemew Tist, wished to bequeath Selastos with some sign of his appreciation. You see, Tist had grown rich in his younger years writing adventure novels glamorizing life out here in Selastos, back when the city's original founders were legendary heroes who endured hardship and fierce Wilderness beasties to bring new wealth to Galitia. Hah! Well, at least someone got rich off this city.

Tist — probably feeling remorseful for getting rich off fabricating the fantastic stories of the founders' bravery and courage — decided to endow Selastos' Council Hall with a clock which would chime the hour and entertain the city folk with a quaint little parade of clockwork glockenspiel figures. Tist commissioned a craftsman called Gorling to construct this clock — leaving him all his wealth to do so — and promptly died.

Although Gorling was well-known in Galitia and Selastos for his mechanical expertise in clock-making, few knew that this profession was really a hobby. Gorling was actually a powerful and secretive sorcerer who saw this opportunity as a chance to secretly control and blackmail certain factions quickly rising to power in Selastos.

Gorling spent a year and a day building the clock you see up there in the Council Hall's tower. He carefully fashioned the clockwork mechanisms, imbuing them with spells and wards so the clock would run forever without ever requiring weights or winding. Prominent businessmen in Selastos even donated gold to plate the clock's hands. But Gorling spent most of his time fashioning the clockwork figures which dance in that balcony beneath the clock, when the great chimes toll the hour.

There! Do you see, as the clock strikes noon, the figures dance about? They twirl to the glockenspiel chimes, dancing around on a spinning platform. Each figure is a miniature of one of the Five Evils which once hounded the city's original founders. There's foul Murder, spinning on his toes, brandishing the bloody knife. Next comes Theft, his lockpicks ready to open any safe, his sack open to receive the booty. See the Gremlin dancing after Theft? He represents everything which can go wrong with machines — from little glitches to complete break-downs. Note the wrench and crowbar that little goblin swings in his hands, waiting to wreak havoc with the railrunners. Next you'll see Fire, a miniature dragon which breaths tiny flames at the Gremlin while he slowly beats his wings, a vain attempt at escaping the clock. And finally, Plague hobbles along, his face decaying beneath his hood, breathing clouds of swamp fumes. And all the while they dance around that central figure on the pedestal, the Doomsayer Prophet, his staff raised as he reads the future in his great book.

But Gorling's clock did not quite work as Tist had planned. For certain, it keeps good time. But instead of tolling the hour, it only chimes at noon and midnight. And only at noon and midnight do the Five Evils dance around the Doomsayer Prophet. And every now and then, when observant and foolish people come out to watch the Doom Clock at midnight, they find that one of the Five Evils is missing from the grim clockwork procession. Would you believe me if I told you each figure could live one night a year, free to roam and inflict their characteristic evil upon the city? No, perhaps that is too tall a tale for old Haldemus to tell. But mark my words, young ragamuffins, when one of the Five Evils misses the Doom Clock's midnight chimes, be certain he is roaming the shadows, waiting to strike.

GORLING'S DOOM CLOCK

The clock in the Council Hall tower was donated by Bartholemew Tist for Selastos' 50th anniversary as a final gesture of good will before the author's death. Many Galitians had read his novels of Selastos' early "heroes" and packed up to head off to the new "city of gold." It's not widely known whether Tist wrote these novels of his own volition, or whether he was well-paid by the city's first Big Rich to create these novels as propaganda to move people out to Selastos. Tist himself never left Galitia.

The author lived out his days in a palatial residence in Galitia, fat from the spoils of his earlier Selastos novels. Perhaps it was out of guilt that he decided to use his wealth to commission the engineer Gorling to fashion the clock for Selastos' Elder Council Hall. What he didn't know was that Gorling was going to make a few additions of his own.

Gorling used his magic — and some say the magic of other sorcerers he enslaved — to imbue the clock with certain magical powers. The clock would never need winding. Its gold-plated hands would always tell the correct time. And its clockwork figures which danced around the form of the Doomsayer Prophet at noon and midnight could come alive.

Few residents of Selastos believe this tale. They simply know that the clock figures sometimes fore-

tell disasters and misfortune. When the figure of one of the Five Evils is missing from the clock at the stroke of midnight, that particular evil will be visited upon someone in Selastos. When the figure of Murder is missing, a prominent citizen is often found the next day with his throat cut. When Theft is absent from the clockwork procession, a valuable item will soon be missing. Gremlin's disappearance is responsible for major breakdowns, and Fire is responsible for those rare conflagrations which decimate entire city blocks. The absence of Plague is perhaps the most feared, since it foretells the outbreak of some virulent sickness in portions of Selastos' population. The Doomsayer Prophet has only gone missing once — just before Selastos' "water war" and the Taxim uprising.

Few know that the figures themselves are the cause of such misfortune.

Each of the six "clockwork" figures in the Doom Clock's mechanical procession is actually an unholy combination of clockwork monstrosity and homunculus. Most of the time they are little more than clockwork figures — fancy machines with padding, clothing and accessories to make them look like midget figures of the Five Evils and the Doomsayer Prophet. But once a year, at night only, they are allowed to come alive and do their masters' bidding. Each figure may miss one midnight chiming while doing its foul mission.

But these homunculi are not free-will beings. Each is controlled by a special control artifact. And only certain prestigious personalities in Selastos possess a controller for one of the Doom Clock's figures.

INSIDE THE CLOCK

The Doom Clock itself is well-protected against both the curious and the ambitious. Gorling and his enslaved mages somehow built the clock into the Council Hall tower with no door, and the only window is the balcony through which the clockwork figures are viewed. Nobody really knows how Gorling got inside or how he transported all the gears, clockwork mechanisms and support material inside.

Few know exactly what kinds of magic spells protect the inner workings of the Doom Clock. Few really care to find out the hard way. The clock has two different levels — an upper level for the actual clock and chime workings, the lower level for the mechanical workings for the platform that spins when the Five Evils process past the balcony window at noon and midnight. No staircase or access trapdoor connects the two levels, and the entire tower is built quite solidly of stone and cement as thick as one meter in some places.

The upper level is apparently crackling with the

Tom ONeill

energies which mysteriously drive the clock without cranking or weights. The few adventuresome (and foolish) types who've tried entering this sealed level through gates or other teleportation magic have often come out fried to a crisp by those energies. Some come out mangled by the clockwork inside. These rare individuals don't usually live long enough to relate how they came to be in such a fried or mangled state …

One would think the Doom Clock's lower level would be easier to enter, since it has a large balcony window through which people can watch the Five Evils parade when the clock chimes twice a day. But the upper and lower edges of the balcony window are lined with short, metal rods tipped in sharp, glistening spikes. Each spike is gold-plated — which sometimes helps mask the shiny blood which occasionally covers some of the spikes. Nobody's really seen it, but some speak of the spikes gnashing from above and below the balcony window on anyone foolish enough to try and enter the Doom Clock through that obvious opening. That might explain the burglar they found there one morning a few years ago, his lifeless corpse hanging limply from the balcony, his head and torso impaled on the lower spikes. The following night, something pulled the body off the spikes and tossed it down into the square below while the clock chimed midnight …

The only figure visible all the time is the Doomsayer Prophet, who stands behind his pulpit with his arms raised in warning at the center of the platform which spins the other figures around. The circular platform leads out of and back into two curtained alcoves on either side of the prophet, concealing the figures of the Five Evils until they parade. Of course, this also prevents folks from seeing whether one of the Five Evils is missing.

As with the upper level, few foolhardy souls have entered the lower level and lived long enough to utter but a few breaths about the experience before dying a grisly death. Some say the lower level is protected by the same crackling energies and mangling gears that protect the upper level. Others weave tales of two immense guardian clockwork knights which hide in the darkened corners of the tower and come alive to dispatch intruders. An even more fantastic tale suggests that the clockwork figures themselves come alive to protect their sanctuary. And while few people believe this story, the corpse of the mage who supposedly used a gate inside the clock's lower level suggests an ounce of truth. His throat had been cut, his foot was missing, he'd been hit over the head with a heavy object, burned, and infected with some rotting disease …

It is not known just how the Doom Clock's figures leave when they are found missing. Some speculate that Gorling built in some kind of secret

passage into the clock tower usable only by his homunculi, although others suspect the figures just climb out through the balcony and are immune to the gold-plated spikes believed to impale others. Several drunks in town claim to have seen Fire actually fly out of the tower on his beating dragon wings, but most dismiss this tale as the ramblings of the intoxicated.

Nobody really knows what happened to Gorling after the clock was set in motion. He seemed to be around long enough to secretly distribute most of the homunculi's controlling artifacts, but then he promptly disappeared. Some say he was consumed by the magic he used to enslave the other sorcerers "helping" him build the clock. Others believe Gorling transformed himself into the Doomsayer Prophet figure, to live eternally and awaken to plot his usual brand of trouble. Another rumor holds that Gorling was ripped apart within his own clock, mangled by the very gears and spells he used to create it.

DOOM CLOCK HOMUNCULI

Gorling was a somewhat crazed Order alchemist from Galitia who practiced his art by night and tinkered with clocks during the day. Nobody really knows why he animated the Doom Clock's figures as clockwork homunculi — some think he had a particular grudge against the citizens of Selastos, while others believe he went truly insane and slipped from the side of Order to that of Chaos.

Perhaps the most believable theory is that he owed large favors to several powerful entities in Selastos — by enslaving one homunculus to each of these powers, it's said that he paid off his debts.

The homunculi were constructed around a base "doll" — each doll was in fact a complex mechanically animated clockwork figure built from specially prepared copper (to allow the homunculus flesh to adhere to its new form). It is rumored that the ingredients for each homunculus differed according to the special abilities Gorling wished to imprint into the creation. No doubt the blood of several Unnaturals was used in each figure, although nobody knows where Gorling found bits of "dragon's wing" to make the Fire figure fly.

Each homunculus is about one meter tall and is relatively humanoid in form — the main exception being Fire, who takes the form of a flame-belching dragon from mythology. Once each homunculus had congealed around its clockwork form, Gorling decorated them with paints and costumes appropriate to each figure. Gold played an important part in these decorations, since Selastos was Tist's "city of gold" and since many prominent citizens donated gold for the Doom Clock's construction. The figures are adorned in gold-trimmed tunics, with gold thread patterns stitched into the hems. Even Fire is covered in shimmering golden scales.

Because they're part homunculus and part clockwork figures, each of the Five Evils is tied to a master. During the month in which each homunculus congealed, Gorling created a control device tied directly to that creature. These devices ranged from the mystical — the knife of a homicidal lunatic for Murder — to the thaumaturgic — a miniature figure of Fire — to the mundane — a greasy old wrench for Gremlin. Nobody can control a Doom Clock figure without its controlling device and the knowledge to use it properly.

The controlling device not only allows a master to manipulate one of the Five Evils, it's also the key to freeing that Evil from the clock tower. While they're in the tower, each figure is an inanimate clockwork figure clothed in a flesh-like substance and decorated in cloth and gold. But the controlling devices ignite the magical energies within each figure. And all the figures are tied to the clock. The clock keeps track of how often they are used. Figures can only be animated once every year for 12 hours — the Five Evils may only miss one chiming of noon or midnight. The Doom Clock's inner workings slowly build the magical energies needed to charge each figure, and store it until use like a sorcerous clock spring.

Each of the five figures has its own advantages suitable to its purposes. However, all the homunculi share the common advantage of a long life span (a CIII Special Ability). While they are within the

Doom Clock, they are inanimate — their living parts are considered to be in a magical stasis. The homunculi are only considered truly alive when they leave the clock to carry out their master's bidding.

The Five Evils all share the same drawbacks. The largest drawbacks are their time limitation and their binding to the clock tower (each considered as a CIV Compensation from list A). Each figure cannot be used more than once a year. If a figure is not used during a year, that magical energy is released on the stroke of midnight on the eve of the new year; it cannot be used twice the following year. Those who hold controlling devices who try to use their figure more than once a year find that the device doesn't work the second time.

The Doom Clock figures are all tied to the clock tower, and cannot leave for more than 12 hours. Most jobs the homunculi are summoned for take less than 12 hours, but occasionally complications arise which make fulfilling an order difficult. In any case, a figure will return to the clock an hour before its 12 hours are up. These homunculi have been known to interrupt their masters' biddings to return to the Doom Clock in time, and sometimes violate their other bindings to harm or murder those who stand in their way. Over time device controllers need to learn what their homunculus is capable of within the 12-hour period. Homunculi who, for whatever reason, do not return to the clock tower by the end of the 12 hours slowly "wind down" — for each hour beyond 12 that they're away from the clock (beginning with hour 13), they lose one of their special abilities and one point from all their attributes. Once they can no longer move to climb back into the tower, they simply flop down lifeless. To date nobody has found a "wound down" Doom Clock homunculus figure. Well, at least nobody's found one and lived to tell about it …

It is not known whether the figures can operate outside of the Selastos city walls — few have tried sending them on errands outside, and most of those who can control the clockwork homunculi know that their magical properties don't mix well with gates.

Because each figure is tied to a master, they are all considered to have the Employed (CIII) Compensation. Each is enslaved to the being who possesses and knows how to operate the controlling device — although they are further limited in what they can do by their special abilities and their quirky sense of purpose.

When animated, the Five Evils and the Doomsayer Prophet are all subject to a variety of drawbacks. Because each is a clockwork homunculus — not quite Human, not fully mechanical — they have minor bigotry against Humans (Bigotry CI). This is manifest as they carry

out their masters' biddings. They tend to regard Humans as most Humans regard insects: as nuisances to be eliminated if they get in the way. However, each figure gets rid of annoying Humans in its own way, according to its magical and thematic nature. Murder might outright kill a Human keeping it from completing its master's orders. Theft might divert a Human by stealing a valuable and taunting that Human into a dangerous situation. Fire would have no qualms about burning an annoying Human, while Gremlin would cause some kind of mechanical disaster to eliminate any Humans standing in its way. Plague is a bit more subtle. Since its methods take time, it can only inflict a Human with disease and hope he goes away — although to many, both Human and Unnatural, the sight of Plague is enough to discourage them from getting in this homunculus' way. The Doomsayer Prophet hasn't been released from the Doom Clock for many years, so few can speculate on how its bigotry against meddling Humans is manifest.

Most residents of Selastos hear the Doom Clock tale at some point in their lives (usually as children), so they're familiar with the spooky legends of the clockwork figures coming to life to wreak misfortune. Those unlucky enough to notice these figures sneaking around the city's shadows shrink back in fear — the homunculi are regarded as minor villains (Infamy CI). As villains, it is not in the average citizen's best interests to involve themselves in the foul dealings of such unholy and dangerous creations. In the same vein, most folks are prejudiced against the figures (Prejudice CII) — the homunculi stick to the shadows when they venture out of the Doom Clock tower, and rarely step into the company of others who might reveal their purpose, keep them from fulfilling their masters' biddings, and publicly revile them. They are out of their element in social situations (Cultural Unfamiliarity CI), and know that darkness and shadow offer their only safety and shelter.

In most cases, the clockwork homunculi cannot understand others and never speak — although it is rumored that the Doomsayer Prophet is the only figure which can speak. The Five Evils can fulfill their duties without speaking, and need understand nobody but their individual controllers (Language CII). And their controllers can only "speak" to the figures through their controlling artifacts. Even then, each controller must be careful how he phrases a homunculus' orders. Each figure's basic purpose is limited by its magical and thematic nature — for instance, Murder won't steal, sabotage machinery or set fire to anything, and Theft won't murder or inflict others with disease. The figures also follow their orders to the letter of the word (Quirk CII), so controllers have to be careful

how they phrase a figure's mission when using their controlling device. An order for Murder to "kill those bastards" would be construed by the homunculus as an order to kill all the bastards it could within 12 hours. Orders must be very specific. Sometimes it seems the homunculi have minds of their own, and they try to find loopholes in their orders to cheat their masters.

When animated, each clockwork homunculus takes on a twisted personality of its own. Those who treat them as simple clockwork figures or fleshy homunculi often pay with their lives — those who remember that the Five Evils are a deadly combination of clockwork creations and homunculi usually just escape with their lives.

MURDER

The clockwork figure of Murder is clothed in black garments characteristic of those worn during the Godwar in Marl's dark ages. Most of these clothes are trimmed in gold thread, and various accessories such as the belt and shoe buckles are also gold. A black cowl hides much of Murder's malevolent face from view, although the tip of its elongated nose pokes out beyond the shadow. In one hand Murder holds a long knife with a jagged edge.

When the clock strikes noon and midnight, Murder spins around on one leg, the other raised as if quietly tiptoeing after its prey. The figure seems to do a morbid jig, all while its knife arm makes stabbing motions, slicing into some unseen victim. Murder is the first clockwork figure to emerge from the Doom Clock's curtain, and its appearance seems to be preceded by a sick-sounding nasal laughter. Some say this sound is actually Murder cackling as it butchers another victim, but most attribute the noise to the screeching gears and clunking clock mechanisms which animate the figures.

Those who believe Murder's clockwork figure is actually an animated homunculus think the sorcerer Gorling constructed it from a mixture of blood and melted flesh taken from several great killers of his day, including Meat Cleaver Max, Brigg the Assassin, and "Violets" McGee. This would easily account for the homunculus' voracious appetite for blood when it is summoned once a year to do its controller's bidding. When given a command, Murder does its best to fulfill its goal while killing as many as it can, mostly those who get in its way. Of all the clockwork homunculi, it's the one which runs the greatest risk of returning late to the clock. Murder spends as much time as it can killing extra people, both before and after the individual specified to die is dispatched. Those people fortunate (or unfortunate) enough to view Murder in action and live to tell about it say the figure laps up its victims' blood as it pools on the ground nearby. While nobody knows if the homunculi requires blood to live, this might simply be an expression of the creature's unholy origins.

Murder's actions are limited to killing a particular individual and other activities required to achieve that goal — including breaking and entering, evading guards, and killing those who discover his presence and evil intent. Its principle function is murder. It cannot kill a victim and steal his most valuable possession, nor can it use anything but its knife to dispatch others.

It is said that Murder uses a paralyzing touch to render its victims helpless (a CIV Advantage with a value of 25) — although the sight of an otherwise inanimate clockwork figure moving toward someone with the intent to kill them might be enough to paralyze victims with abject terror. The figure has apparently learned much in the art of murder, sneaking around, and tracking its prey. Murder doesn't need to personally know its victim, it just has an uncanny ability to identify and find the target. The figure's knife is rumored to be the same one the infamous "Violets" used to disembowel her family. It is particularly sharp, and some believe it to be imbued with some kind of sharpening spell which increases its effectiveness. The knife is permanently attached to Murder's hand, and has never been seen free from the dwarf's little fist.

MURDER

AGILITY 10
Acrobatics 12, climbing 13, dodge 12, melee combat 16, stealth 15
DEXTERITY 10
Lock picking 13
ENDURANCE 8
Resist shock 10
STRENGTH 9
TOUGHNESS 9
INTELLECT 8
Perception 11, tracking 12
MIND 8
CONFIDENCE 10
Intimidation 23, willpower 15
CHARISMA 7
Charm (25), persuasion (27), taunt (17)
Life Points: 3
Equipment: Knife, damage value STR+7/20
Roleplaying Notes:
When encountered, Murder keeps to the shadows, al-

Tom ONeill

though it often laughs to itself in an insane, nasal giggle. It won't chase down characters unless it has a clear opportunity to murder or harm them, or unless they try to keep it from performing its mission. Of course, if Murder has been ordered to kill one of the characters, it does everything in its power to accomplish its goal, even murdering a character's companions.

MURDER'S CONTROLLER

Murder's controlling device is in the hands of Selastos' most powerful man, Jon Able. Able owns AbleMines, Able Tool and Able Car & Cart, all businesses relied on by other powerful entities within the city. Able keeps Murder's controlling device — a virtual replica of "Violets" McGee's knife — locked away in the vaults of his estate. On the rare occasion when Able needs one of his competitors or a meddling gumshoe eliminated, he must use the knife to slay a small animal (a rat often does nicely) while reciting the command he wants the clockwork homunculus to follow.

Able rarely uses Murder to do his bidding. He's a powerful enough man that he can resort to other means to get his way, and he has powerful resources at his command. To abuse Murder's power by using it every year to eliminate a rival or the occasional thorn in his side would be too easy for Able — and it might look suspicious to others.

However, Able's recent fascination with the Oathbreaker Chaotics and his delving into the realm of necromancy have made him more vulnerable and more apt to depend on Murder to keep him clear of suspicious activity. These interests are slowly draining his discretion and better judgment when it comes to managing his legitimate businesses and his shadowy activities. If his identity as a prominent businessman and leader were to come into question by an individual, Able might not hesitate to have that person eliminated during a visit from Murder …

Few know for certain where Able got Murder's controlling artifact. Those who know about it don't talk much of it, although many speculators believe McGee's knife has been in Able's family since the Doom Clock was constructed. Some say that Gorling himself presented the knife to Able's grandfather after the blade mysteriously disappeared from a sentinel evidence room.

THEFT

The figure of Theft is a dwarfish little man with brown clothes trimmed in gold thread. It wears a flat little hat with a brim and a black mask tied around its eyes. Theft looks like any of the innumerable stereotypical street thieves to be found in Selastos' alleys. Theft follows Murder, as it is the second figure to skip out when the Doom Clock strikes noon and midnight. As it tip-toes along as if sneaking, Theft waves its lockpick in one hand while brandishing the open bag in the other, waiting to scoop up the loot and disappear into the shadows.

Like the other clockwork homunculi, Theft is subject to certain limitations of character and ability. Its primary purpose is to steal items from others and deliver them to its controller before returning to the Doom Clock tower. It cannot directly harm individuals through combat, although it is known to have caused diversions to distract others. It is capable of stealing only those items which it can fit into its bag or carry on its back. Theft prefers to stay in shadow — if it isn't seen, it can go about its business without outside interference. Some say Gorling congealed this homunculus from Human and cat blood, possibly the only reason it's the most predictable of the Five Evils. Unlike Murder and its fellows, Theft has no twisted impulse to distort its controller's orders.

Theft is adept at climbing walls, wriggling through tight windows, and busting locks and safes to get its booty. Its activities are often dismissed as that creaking floorboard, a flitting shadow, or the unlatched window banging in the wind.

Theft has the CIV Special Abilities of "confusion" and "darkness" to help it

Tom ONeill

enter areas unseen, steal its loot and evade capture. It relies on its other skills to get its jobs done. Some believe that Theft and Gremlin remained animated for some time after their creation and before they were installed in the Doom Clock — during this time Gorling trained both in their particular specialities.

THEFT

AGILITY 10
Acrobatics 14, climbing 16, dodge 12, running 13, stealth 16, unarmed combat 11
DEXTERITY 12
Lock picking 18
ENDURANCE 8
STRENGTH 8
TOUGHNESS 9
INTELLECT 10
Perception 14, safe cracking 16
MIND 8
CONFIDENCE 8
Intimidation 14, willpower 12
CHARISMA 7
Charm (25), persuasion (27), taunt (17)
Life Points: 3
Equipment: Lockpick set (adds +3 to *lock picking* skill)

Roleplaying Notes: Theft is the least dangerous of the Five Evils. When encountered, it attempts to hide and escape rather than confront characters. Theft relies on its powers of darkness and confusion to evade others. If encountered while in the middle of a job, Theft tries to divert characters away from the scene long enough to complete his break-in.

THEFT'S CONTROLLER

The artifact which controls Theft is a large gold-plated padlock with a key inserted into the hole. The key cannot be removed from the lock — it is part of the complex mechanical and magical mechanism which controls Theft. To rouse Theft from his place within the Doom

Clock, one must turn the key until the padlock unlocks, then speak the order Theft must follow.

Nobody knows for certain who possesses Theft's controlling device, but many suspect a high-level Selastos sentinel detective keeps it as a paperweight on his disheveled office desk. Theft is perhaps the least malevolent of the Five Evils in its inherent purpose, so it would make sense that the homunculus served a somewhat law-abiding individual. This might also account for a seemingly annual occurrence where damning evidence was mysteriously produced for a certain important criminal case.

GREMLIN

The Doom Clock's third figure is Gremlin, the third of the Five Evils. Gremlin is a green-skinned, leering-faced monstrosity dressed up in a mechanic's coveralls and sporting a jester's cap. Its clothing is all bordered with gold thread, and some of its tools are plated in gold. In one hand it brandishes an oversized wrench, while in the other it holds a large crowbar. A gold-plated can of oil and a machinist's tool pouch hang from its belt. Gremlin's face is green and shaped with the elongated pointy nose of a goblin. Skewed teeth protrude from its rubbery lips, and pointed ears stick out from beneath the jester hat's rim.

When Gremlin emerges in the Doom Clock's procession, he alternately seems to tip-toe and skip about on one foot, swinging his wrench and crowbar in a comic dance. If the sun is out, the gold adorning Gremlin sparkles, giving the figure a shimmering quality which makes it seem that parts of the Gremlin are invisible at times.

Gremlin is in fact a clockwork homunculus well-trained in mechanics. Once a year its controller can order it to sabotage some piece of equipment, either to effect a delay, aid in a burglary, or to murder an individual in the typical mechanical "accident." Rumors speculate that this homunculus was created from a soupy mixture of Ghoul flesh and the blood of one of the finest mechanics in Galitia — who, of course, mysteriously disappeared around the time of the Doom Clock's construction.

Gremlin is said to have been the first clockwork homunculus Gorling decanted, to give him the appropriate amount of training. While Gremlin has the innate powers to turn himself invisible (a CIV Special Ability which adds +10 to any *stealth* totals), it relies on its extensive mechanical training and its tools to accomplish its sabotage goals. The homunculus' inner orders are to cause malfunctions in machinery without being noticed. But while its activities are limited to a mechanical nature, Gremlin is not above a little mischief of his own during his annual 12 hours outside the Doom Clock. It is fond of misinterpreting its orders, and

enjoys sabotaging other equipment on its way to and from a job. Gremlin has no scruples about injuring or killing anyone who stands in its way, or just happens to be around when it gets into a nasty mood. When Gremlin does his work, most of Selastos hears about it the next day — the news usually consists of some large-scale mechanical disaster (a major railrunner disaster, for instance) accompanied by a wave of several smaller mishaps and a stream of reports involving people attacked from the shadows and a few unlucky souls bludgeoned to death by a heavy tool or eviscerated with what must have been the sharp hook-end of a crowbar. Some say this twisted behavior is a direct result of Gorling congealing Gremlin first. Perhaps the sorcerer was in a hurry — more likely this was his first attempt at a homunculus incorporating the clockwork "doll" around which the flesh formed.

Despite his mechanical training, Gremlin causes much of his damage by bending parts with blows from its wrench, applying generous amounts of oil to vehicles' brakes, and ripping out gears with its crowbar. Although it might be invisible, Gremlin is anything but quiet about his business.

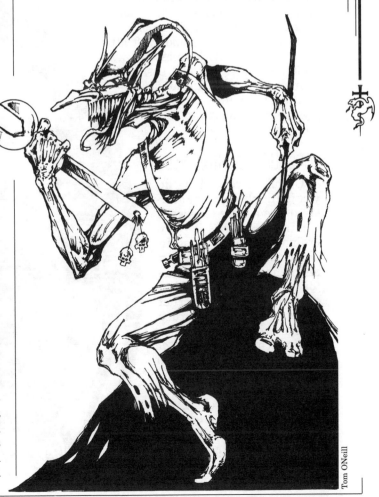

Tom ONeill

GREMLIN

AGILITY 9
Acrobatics 12, climbing 13, dodge 11, melee combat 13, stealth 14, unarmed combat 12
DEXTERITY 10
Lock picking 14, vehicle piloting: wheeled 15
ENDURANCE 8
STRENGTH 8
Lifting 12
TOUGHNESS 9
INTELLECT 10
Demolitions 13, perception 12, tracking 13, vehicle mechanic: wheeled 17
MIND 8
CONFIDENCE 8
Intimidation 13, willpower 10
CHARISMA 6
Charm (25), persuasion (27), taunt (17)
Life Points: 3
Equipment: Can of oil; crowbar, damage value STR+7/22; machinist's tool pouch; wrench, damage value STR+5/20

Roleplaying Notes: Gremlin is easily distracted from its work when characters encounter it. Gremlin views others as fun machines to destroy ... and often does so by attacking from the shadows, crowbar and wrench swinging wildly. It favors a hit-and-fade attack, becoming visible for a blurred moment and swift attack, then retreating into darkness and invisibility. Although it could easily kill characters by devising some devious mechanical failure, Gremlin enjoys murder enough to carry it out himself.

GREMLIN'S CONTROLLER

Gremlin's controlling device is a duplicate of the oversized wrench the clockwork homunculus carries. It's very ordinary and easy to lose. In order to activate Gremlin and deliver orders, its master must smash some kind of mechanical construct while speaking the order. Clocks seem to be the best mechanical constructs to destroy when using the wrench, an ironic twist on Gremlin's true nature.

Gremlin's controlling wrench is in the hands of crook Norbert Rees, who runs half of Selastos' gambling and whoring dens. Rees has a tendency towards filling his ranks with Unnaturals, and Gremlin takes that one step further. Rees doesn't use Gremlin too often — sometimes he's called upon by his influential industrial backers to use the homunculus on their behalf, and he doesn't want to look bad by using Gremlin too often for his own purposes. When Rees use Gremlin for his own ends, it's usually in retaliation for something his competitor and former lieutenant, Jervis Belasc, has done. Last year's Breaker Street whorehouse massacre — one of Belasc's attacks against Rees — was quickly followed by a factory accident in which Belasc's right hand sorcerer was sucked up and mangled by a particularly evil-looking piece of mining equipment ...

FIRE

Fire is perhaps the most simple-minded of all the Doom Clock's homunculi. Unlike its companions, it is not humanoid-shaped, nor does it think like a humanoid. The fourth of the Five Evils, Fire's clockwork figure is that of an ancient fire-breathing dragon.

When the clock chimes and the Five Evils dance around the Doomsayer Prophet, Fire cranes its neck and spouts a miniature plume of flame from its nostrils, its teeth gnashing, its gold-scaled wings beating the air and one of its sharp claws lunging out at Gremlin ahead of it. It is a fierce monstrosity constructed of gold scales — a figure of horror left over from the last Godwar, a fatted serpent with razor claws and bat wings. Fire is the favorite clockwork figure of children, since it glitters with gold and spits flame as it spins around the Doom Clock.

Fire is indeed a terrible apparition, especially to those few unfortunate souls who happen to view it on the rare occasions it ventures from its perch in the Doom Clock to undertake its master's bidding. While most of the other homunculi function with the twisted rationale of Humans, Fire follows the bestial urges of the terrible dragons of yore. Rumors say Gorling constructed Fire from bits of ground flesh from an ancient, petrified dragon he found in some dismal corner of the Dirak

Tom O'Neill

Desert. Others believe the sorcerer simply found Unnaturals with Fire's traits and incorporated their blood in the stew from which the clockwork homunculus was congealed.

Fire has only one purpose when summoned — to set things ablaze. Its master often gives it a specific target to torch, but Fire tends to go on a rampage whenever it's temporarily released from the Doom Clock. Fire always destroys its objective in a very visible and destructive conflagration. Along the way it sets smaller fires and attacks anyone unlucky enough to attract its attention. Since it is one of the more destructive of the Five Evils, Fire's controller rarely uses the homunculus. When Fire flies from the Doom Clock tower, folks expect entire city blocks to go up in flames …

The dragon homunculus has the ability to fly despite the weight of its inner clockwork mechanisms, and can breath streams of fiery liquid (something like gasoline set on fire) — both are considered CIV Special Abilities. Its tough, armor scale skin is equal to +6/21 armor, and its teeth and claws are sharp as the best honed knives. Although Fire depends on its flaming breath to cause the most damage, it sometimes resorts to using its teeth and claws when confronted in close combat.

FIRE

AGILITY 10
Flight: winged 15, melee combat 13
DEXTERITY 10
Fire breathing 15
ENDURANCE 10
Resist shock 13
STRENGTH 9
TOUGHNESS 10
INTELLECT 8
Perception 11, tracking 12
MIND 8
CONFIDENCE 8
Intimidation 17, willpower 13
CHARISMA 7
Charm (30), persuasion (30), taunt (15)
Life Points: 3
Natural Tools: Claws, damage value STR+4/19; fire breath, damage value 10; teeth, damage value STR+4/19; armored scale hide, armor value TOU+6/16

Roleplaying Notes: Fire generally avoids characters when it can, relying on its ability to fly to escape. However, if cornered, it turns to attack, first blasting characters with its fiery breath, then closing to slash with its claws and teeth. If retreating, Fire tends to set everything in sight ablaze, then flies away to safety.

FIRE'S CONTROLLER

The controlling device for Fire is a miniature of the dragon figure in the Doom Clock. The figure stands no more than 12 centimeters high, and is gilded in the same shades of gold as the original homunculus. Its eyes are tiny rubies, and its claws and teeth are fashioned from polished ivory — or perhaps from true dragon claws and teeth, if one believes speculation.

To command Fire, its controller must move the little figures wings as if it's flying — for being so small, the miniature Fire is very articulate. The wing mechanisms release an amount of flammable gas stored within the figure's belly, and the controller must use a lit match to ignite the gas as it jets out the little dragon's nostrils. Once the flame is lit, the controller must state his commands. The master knows the homunculus has acknowledged his orders and has become animated to carry them out when the tiny flame disappears.

Speculators believe that Theosophus — the firemage who controls the Quarter-Moon Street political machine and runs the Council of Elders — has Fire's controlling artifact. The mage reportedly keeps the miniature metal dragon on the mantle above the fireplace in his estate, although few visitors to the place could confirm such a rumor. It's a rather conspicuous place to hide one of the Doom Clock homunculi's controllers — but most folks say Theosophus isn't stupid enough to display it so prominently without magical protection. Those few who know the firemage has the device believe he's cast some sort of spell over it allowing the figure to animate itself if ever endangered.

Theosophus has enough power through Quarter-Moon Street and the Council of Elders that he doesn't need Fire to have his way in Selastos. He's rarely used the clockwork homunculus. The firemage prefers to rely on more tried and true methods of enforcement, blackmail and control to manipulate Selastos city government. However, one never knows when some rube will come along and get Theosophus upset. Some reporters are still trying to uncover the arson conspiracy surrounding that gung-ho Council of Elders candidate whose entire block burned to the ground 10 years ago …

PLAGUE

The ugliest of the Five Evils, Plague is the last in the Doom Clock's mechanical procession. This hooded dwarf figure hides behind the tattered folds of a gold-trimmed robe and cloak. Only the remains of a scarred nose poke out past the shadow. In its rotted flesh hands Plague brandishes a harvesting scythe with a golden blade coated in red paint (or blood, nobody's certain). At the appointed hours,

Plague follows the Doom Clock's procession, slashing downward with its scythe and spinning on unseen footing.

Plague represents the disease known as the Scourge which swept over Marl after the last Godwar. Legends say that the disease rose from the dead corpses which festered and rotted on the battlefield. Some say the Scourge was the dead's revenge on those who had slain them, although more recent and learned scholars speculate that the disease was connected to unsanitary conditions.

The clockwork homunculus of Plague can be activated to infect a certain individual with the Scourge. Unlike Murder, Plague only infects its initial victim, although it's not prohibited from striking at others who get in its way. It does not wantonly spread its disease — the Scourge does that on its own.

Plague is last in line for the Doom Clock's procession for a good reason — it's "downwind" from the other homunculi, who fear they, too, might contract the Scourge from Plague's own rotting hands. While the Plague homunculus wouldn't infect its fellows, its touch is still deadly to other living beings.

Plague has a CIV Special Ability called "plague touch" which it uses to spread the Scourge. To infect others, Plague needs to make a successful hit with its scythe or with its rotting hand. While these attacks cause normal damage, symptoms of the Scourge do not appear until the next morning. Symptoms include a progressive weakness, and a pallid skin tone. As the disease eats through the body, flesh loses its pink color and turns gray and mushy, as if part of a rotting corpse. The Scourge causes its victim to lose four attribute points per day until the victim has no more attribute points and dies. Although the Scourge can be treated through a combination of medicine and sorcery, its victims never recover past the point at which the plague is healed.

Worse yet, anyone the initial victim touches after being hit with plague touch also contracts the Scourge — and anyone touching that person contracts

the Scourge … Luckily the Scourge only affects living corporeal beings. Because the disease is so uncontrollable, Plague has rarely been summoned to infect an individual. The last time it was used was 15 years ago, just after the sentinels raided a hidden temple of Saer and massacred those followers found sacrificing innocents within.

PLAGUE

AGILITY 9
Climbing 11, dodge 11, melee combat 15, melee parry 14, stealth 15
DEXTERITY 9
ENDURANCE 10
Resist shock 12
STRENGTH 10
TOUGHNESS 11
INTELLECT 8
Perception 12
MIND 8
CONFIDENCE 8
Intimidation 28, willpower 13
CHARISMA 5
Charm (25), persuasion (27), taunt (17)

Life Points: 3
Equipment: Scythe, damage value STR+6/18

Roleplaying Notes: Plague would rather avoid confrontation whenever possible. It hunts down its intended victim, but works around those standing in its way. Plague resorts to attacks from the shadows only when there is no other option around adversaries. When it can, it likes to hide until its victim passes close by — then it gently touches its victim with a rotting hand, infecting the victim with its plague touch.

PLAGUE'S CONTROLLER

The artifact which controls the Plague homunculus is a mummified hand with the index finger pointing out, as if singling out a victim. To command Plague to in-

Tom ONeill

fect an individual, its master must find an image of the victim (a photograph or accurate drawing will do) and rub the mummified hand's finger over the image. The following morning the victim often wakes showing symptoms of the Scourge. If he isn't isolated, the victim will infect many people in the neighborhood as the Scourge swiftly spreads.

Plague's mummified hand was last reported to be in possession of the Cult of Saer. Apparently Gorling thought Plague's effects chaotic enough to appeal to the cult, and presented the hand to the cult's leader when the Doom Clock was completed. Then again, perhaps the cult heard of the Scourge the Plague homunculus could spread and stole the hand from Gorling ...

However, after the sentinel raid 15 years ago, the hand was lost. The Cult of Saer has occasionally increased search efforts for the mummified hand, but so far has not managed to recover the artifact. Some believe the hand is buried with the remains of the secret underground temple where the sentinels massacred cult followers. This rumor would coincide with other tales that the high priest of Saer killed at the massacre delivered a final curse on the city before he died. Others are certain the sentinels took the hand for their own purposes. One thing is certain — Plague has not been missing from his post in the Doom Clock for 15 years.

DOOMSAYER PROPHET

The dwarfish figure of the Doomsayer Prophet is different from the Doom Clock's other figures of the Five Evils in several ways. The prophet is always visible standing behind his pulpit, reading from his great Book of Days and warning of the future with his arms raised. When the other figures emerge to dance around the Doom Clock, the prophet raises his arms and the pages of the book turn. And when the Doomsayer Prophet goes missing from his post, it is almost immediately noticed.

The prophet is dressed in fine gold-woven robes inscribed with stitched prophesies in an ancient and forgotten language. A large hat sits upon his head, and his gray curls cascade from beneath the hat, forming a flowing beard which reaches below the level of the pulpit. His face is stern and angry, as if rebuking those who doubt his prophesies. In his right hand the prophet holds a wooden staff with a golden point at bottom and a golden headpiece at the top. His left hand points ominously to the pages of the Book of Days.

The title of doomsayer prophet was given to those individuals in Marl's ancient days who had the ability to see the future. These sages included those seers from the medieval court astrologers to the village wise man. They mostly foretold of minor events which would affect their domain. But all

ADVENTURE IDEA: THE "HAND OF FATE"

The characters are hired by a mysterious and superstitious patron who asks them to recover an ancient treasure sacred to her people. She provides them with clues and a map showing portions of Selastos' underground areas where she believes the "Hand of Fate" was lost, and promises a substantial sum should the characters retrieve this treasure.

Their search leads them on a dangerous crawl through Selastos' infested sewers, into trapped passages and through the hideous remains of a secret chapel filled with the old remains of cultists and sentinels. They must search through this morbid temple — obviously used for Human sacrifices — and must defeat the temple's monstrous guardian before recovering the "Hand of Fate," little more than a charred and shriveled mummified hand.

But before they can return their prize to their patron, the characters are ambushed in the underground passages by a rival group bent on stealing the artifact for themselves. Once they survive the ambush, the characters can escape from the catacombs and return to Selastos' surface.

The patron could be a high priestess from the Cult of Saer, bent on increasing her prestige within the cult by retrieving the mummified hand which controls the Plague homunculus. Or the woman could represent another party — perhaps one with a more evil purpose — interested in acquiring the controlling artifact to wreak havoc throughout the city by inflicting the deadly Scourge on Selastos. Either way, the woman's associates are lurking nearby, prepared to eliminate the characters and any knowledge that Plague's controlling artifact is lost no more.

doomsayer prophets recognized signs of the coming Godwar. They cried their warnings to peasants and kings, and were ridiculed as crazed idiots. The prophets were cast from their positions of respect and power, and, like most of Marl, were consumed in the horrors of the Godwar.

The figure of the Doomsayer Prophet residing in the Selastos Doom Clock represents those seers of old and the frightening misfortunes they predicted. It was Gorling's final addition to the clock, meant to remind people to listen to warnings. Some say Gorling created this clockwork homunculus to make up for the Five Evils the sorcerer brought to life.

ADVENTURE IDEA: THE BOOKS OF DOOM

Stirring news! A mining crew working a long-abandoned shaft in the nearby gold mines discovered an ancient chest containing the last known Book of Days on Marl! A heavily guarded caravan is returning the book to Selastos, where it will be displayed under lock and key at the city library.

The characters are hired by a mysterious contact to steal the book. The caravan will pass through the city gates and along several streets before arriving at the library. Their patron provides them with exact times and locations for the caravan's route. To avoid anxious crowds, the book is not being brought into the city until the early morning hours — the perfect time for an ambush.

The ambush is much easier than the characters expected — almost too easy. The guards run away or give up, and the locked carriage holding the chest and book is easy to break into. But once inside, the characters find out that the Book of Days is no longer inside the chest!

The next morning, the streetsingers are all telling about the appearance of not one Book of Days, but five which have mysteriously shown up throughout Selastos! The characters' patron approaches them again. Now he wants the characters to find out which of the five books is real and steal that one. The characters become involved in a wild goose chase, running after leads and finding several books — all of which are complete fakes!

This plan was ordered by Theosophus, the firemage who runs the Selastos Council of Elders and the Quarter-Moon Street political machine. Theosophus wants to find out who has the artifacts which control the other Doom Clock homunculi — he figures anyone who already has a controlling artifact knows how powerful their homunculus is, and naturally would want to control as many of the homunculi as possible.

Others think Gorling created this homunculus as a vessel where his soul could reside after his death, watching over the affairs going on within the Selastos Council Hall and looking out over the city's buildings.

When summoned by its master, the Doomsayer Prophet reveals some vision of the future — more often, it warns of disastrous events to come. The last time it was summoned, the homunculus predicted the strife in Selastos which came with the "water war" and the Taxim uprising.

Unlike its fellows within the Doom Clock, the prophet is the only clockwork homunculus Gorling created with the ability to speak, and it speaks rather eloquently for a sorcerous construct. When summoned to deliver its grim predictions, the Doomsayer Prophet does not report directly to its master. Instead, it wanders the back streets of Selastos, preaching its foreboding message to the city's lowlife. It cries out its message in the bars, alleys and diners, exhorting people to prepare for the coming changes. In some cases, people claim that the prophet shapes the future as well as predicts it. This theory is strongly held by those who felt that the Taxim were too stupid and unimaginative to think of striking — these people believe the Doomsayer Prophet stirred up trouble among Selastos' Taxim and drove them to strike, thus fulfilling the homunculus' own prophecy.

Others feel that the Doomsayer Prophet reveals what it reads in its Book of Days. Many cults on Marl believe in some kind of book or scroll or stone upon which is written all the happenings of the past, present and future. This revelation of destiny is said to be given only to those special individuals named the doomsayer prophets. And there are many who think the book sitting on the Doomsayer Prophet's pulpit within the Doom Clock is the last surviving Book of Days in all of Marl. But although many careful observers claim to see writing in the Doomsayer Prophet's Book of Days, all the pages are absolutely blank.

DOOMSAYER PROPHET

AGILITY 8
Climbing 12, stealth 13
DEXTERITY 8
ENDURANCE 8
STRENGTH 8
TOUGHNESS 9
INTELLECT 9
Deduction 13, divination: prophecy 16, perception 12
MIND 9
Hypnotism 13
CONFIDENCE 10
Intimidation 15, streetwise 12, willpower 13
CHARISMA 10
Persuasion 14
Life Points: 3
Roleplaying Notes: When activated, the

Doomsayer Prophet wanders the streets of Selastos, shouting out his prophecies in an intimidating voice. While most residents avoid him, some characters and others might wish to confront this figure. The homunculus simply responds by trying to *intimidate* those who oppose him, or *persuading* or *hypnotizing* them to follow his beliefs. The Doomsayer Prophet relies on the mystique and respect surrounding his position more than any other ability.

DOOMSAYER PROPHET'S CONTROLLER

Rumors abound that the Doomsayer Prophet's controlling device is a thick replica of the Book of Days found on the homunculus' pulpit. Those who believe the tome is an actual Book of Days think that the master must read aloud the specific event foretold in the book for the Doomsayer Prophet to announce warn about it in the streets — or cause it to happen himself. Those who think the prophet's book is completely blank believe the master writes the specific prophecy in his blank book, then reads it out loud so the Doomsayer Prophet can announce it.

There are some people who believe the Doomsayer Prophet is the only one of Gorling's homunculi which doesn't have a controller. These folks think the prophet is the "leader" of the other clockwork homunculi, or believe that the figure of the prophet holds Gorling's soul.

Nobody knows the real story behind the Doomsayer Prophet — just as few know the true background of the Selastos Doom Clock. But everyone knows the fantastic tales. When a Doom Clock figure is missing at noon or midnight, ominous events are about to happen.

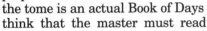

Tom ONeill

CHAPTER TWO

ALBREDURA: LEGENDS OF THE SOUTHLANDS

Greetings, esteemed visitor! Welcome to our fair city. This is Albredura — but of course you already know that. Anyone who would brave the Wilderness to visit another city knows where they are going, hmmm? My name is Samuel Horvath, and I am the top wayman in town.

If there is anything in particular you would like to know, I'm the one who can tell you about it. I can recommend a number of excellent restaurants, or perhaps you would like to know about the best places to shop. Or if it's sightseeing you'd like to do …

What's that, you say? You're interested in the more esoteric parts of town, hmmm? Well, let me think a moment. There are a number of places that have a peculiar history, or at least have some sort of strange story associated with them. Perhaps you have a particular interest, something with which to narrow the choices, hmmm? Please, think about it for a moment, and I'll be right back to assist you.

SAMUEL HORVATH, WAYMAN

AGILITY 9
DEXTERITY 8
ENDURANCE 8
STRENGTH 7
TOUGHNESS 9
INTELLECT 10
Deduction 11, perception 11
MIND 10
Cartography 12, research 13, scholar: Albredura 15
CONFIDENCE 8
Bribery 9, con 9
CHARISMA 9
Charm 10, persuasion 10
Life Points: 4
Equipment: Nice suit; 105 marks
Description: Horvath is a knowledgeable, and generally helpful, wayman. Although not the best wayman around, as he claims, he is very effective. However, he always seems a bit smug and supercilious, traits which lead people to trust him less than they normally would. If pressed, his clients might not be able to put their finger

THE WAYMAN EXPLAINED

Just as the cities of Marl are widely separated by distance and the Wilderness, so too are the underlying social structures a widely disparate lot. The laws, traditions and customs of each city, as well as its currency, can vary greatly from one to the other. Such variety makes it very difficult for the occasional traveler to get his bearings when visiting another city. And on Marl such unfamiliarity can be a recipe for disaster.

So what is the traveler to do? Enter the wayman. He or she is a person well-versed in the customs of their city and, often, familiar with those of other cities. The business of the wayman (the term applies to both men and women) is to, figuratively, show visitors their way around town. In the course of their business dealings, waymen find out information about the cities travelers come from. The wayman's stock in trade is information — the more he has, the better.

Most visitors need to know some basic information upon arriving at a city, such as what the local currency is and the current exchange rates, or the location of a good hotel or inn, or what types of restrictions the law imposes that might affect visitors (for instance, the fact that gasoline-powered vehicles are not permitted within the walls of Gimm). A businessman seeking to set up business in the city might need to know what zoning restrictions are in effect, what the tax situation is, what paperwork needs to be completed and just how members of the city council view his type of business.

In addition, a wayman can provide information for tourists interested in seeing the sights — where to go for entertainment, or what is the historical significance of various sites. Many waymen are well-versed in the city's history, as well as the legends and stories of the region. A wayman is a combination travel agent/tour guide/historian/rumormonger/sage.

Of course, there is a fee attached to all this. This ranges from reasonable — 10 to 20 marks — for everyday information (currency, exchange rate, hotels, restrictions, etc.), to exorbitant — 200 or more marks — for hard-to-find information (what gangs are currently in power or which influential people have things to hide). Prices will vary up and down the scale for information in the middle (like the businessman's basic info, which might go for 50 to 80 marks). The difference depends on what type of information is desired, how difficult it is to come by, and how much information is actually required (just the zoning and tax information will cost less than the whole package of necessary information).

Most waymen deal only in everyday information and history, however. Not many have (or want) access to the really secret facts. They are basically guides, greeting people to their city and trying to smooth the transition to a new milieu. Some may actually serve as guides, showing travelers around town, but will charge additional fees for such a service.

Waymen can be found listed in most cities' phone books or through advertisements in the local papers, and many of them maintain offices near one or more gates of their city.

---

on what it is that bothers them about Horvath, but their general feeling is to finish their business and leave as quickly as possible.

THE SKINNY

Say, buddy. Yeah, you, the out-of-towner. My name is Holshaque, Karl Holshaque. Hey, hold on a minute; don't rush off. I can help you. I'm a reporter, and I've been around this burg a long time. Listen, I got the real skinny — you know, the inside dope — for ya. That Horvath, he's an okay guy, and if you want some hard information about Albredura, he's as good as they come. But when it comes to the behind-the-scenes stuff, the things that lurk just beyond the threshold of perception, well then he's just out of his league. He talks about the legends and the dark mysteries, but all he's got are the commonly accepted versions, good for the rubes — I mean, the visitors to our fair town. Now me, *I* can tell you what really happened …

KARL HOLSHAQUE
AGILITY 8
Dodge 16, maneuver 12
DEXTERITY 8
Fire combat 10, lock picking 11
ENDURANCE 8
STRENGTH 8
TOUGHNESS 9
INTELLECT 9
Cantrips 11, deduction 16, perception 12 (find 14) (evidence analysis 14)
MIND 10
Research 15, scholar: Albredura 16
CONFIDENCE 9
Alteration: vitomancy 12, con 13, intimidation 11, streetwise 15

CHARISMA 8
Persuasion 11, taunt 10
Life Points: 9
Spells: *Facade, intuition*
Cantrips: *Breeze, candle, chill, find*
Arcane Knowledges: Living forces 3
Equipment: Scribepad; camera; battered hat; rumpled suit
Description: Holshaque is a dedicated, and thereby usually annoying, reporter, who is tenacious in his pursuit of a story. He has an extensive network of "spies," from streetsingers to sources in the coroner's office and the Sentinel Department.

THE OPPOSITE SAX

So, you say you're interested in music, hmmm? Well, there are a number of swinging night spots in town. Some that come to mind are the Midnight Star, the Topaz Room, Paulie's Pentagram, … Oh, well, if you're not interested in tripping the light fantastic; perhaps you'd rather hear about some of these clubs, hmmm?

There is a tale told about a club that once was located in Marketwall. It was known as the Sultry Siren, and it was a pretty popular spot. It was run by one Marcus Kingston, and he kept the crowds coming back with a top-notch band and some of the best torch singers around. But his real treasure was his headliner, Sally Sutherland. She could draw a crowd like there was no tomorrow …

Things went well for quite some time, but all good things are doomed from the beginning, hmmm? Somewhere along the line one of the bandmembers, a saxophone player by the name of Bert Capricus, got all sweet on Sally. Now, Sally didn't have much in her life. She was orphaned early and managed to eke out an existence on the streets. Eventually she got some regular jobs as a streetsinger for different papers, until she hooked up with the *Shining Star* — this was before Tavist Roon got his hands on it and drove the other papers out of business.

While 'singing for the *Star* one day, she was discovered by Marcus Kingston. He took her in, prettied her up and gave her a chance singing in the Siren. She proved to be a big hit, and Kingston took care of her from that day on. He treated her like a daughter. He set her up in her own place, and she sang her heart out for him each night. But then Capricus came along. Sally hadn't had much love in her life, and he was a sweet guy who treated her right, so she fell hard for him.

That didn't sit too good with old Marcus. It wasn't so much that he'd lose his singer — Sally continued to perform, and she and Bert became quite an item at the Siren. No, they say that at some point Marcus Kingston didn't see Sally as a daughter anymore, but got his own heart hooked on her sad songs and her

pretty face. Not only did he want her for himself, but hadn't he given her everything she had, and made her everything she was?

Now, things might have developed differently if this was just a regular love triangle, with the young musician and the older gent vying for the hand of the lovely Sally. But Marcus Kingston was different. You see, some say he was a Vampire. All I know is he must have been very clever to last so long in Albredura, seeing as how we don't countenance anything Unnatural in this city. But this is how the story goes, so let's accept that assumption for now, hmmm?

At any rate, Marcus wanted Sally for himself, so he gave Bert the boot, banned him from the club, and forbade her from seeing him again. Of course, that didn't work. She still slipped out to see him, and they tried to keep things on the sly. But Marcus found out, and when he did, he hit the roof. He flew into a rage and pretty much tore his office apart before he could be calmed down.

After that, things got strange for Bert. The next time he tried to meet Sally, she didn't show up. After a couple of times, he got daring and tried to get into the Sultry Siren to see her. He was persistent and sneaky enough and actually got in. But when he found Sally, it was as if she didn't know who he was. She told him to leave her alone and never come back. Bert was stunned, but he could see that something was very wrong. Sally wasn't acting like herself — it was as if she were in a trance or something. He tried to break her out of it, but she just screamed for help.

That brought Kingston and his goons running. While his men held Bert down, kicking and screaming, Marcus showed him just how much Sally was his, body *and* soul. Then his goons took Bert to another part of town, beat him to within an inch of his life, and left him bleeding and battered in a back alley. No one knows why he didn't just have Bert iced. Maybe Marcus enjoyed the anguish he was inflicting on the young man, or perhaps he was so secure in his power that he didn't feel the need to drain him and throw the dried husk into the nearest dumpster, hmmm? Whatever the reason, it proved to be his downfall.

You see, Bert had a background in magic. He wasn't very adept at it himself, but he had a lot of connections in Magic Circle, the mages' part of town. Bert wanted to get back at Marcus Kingston, wanted him to feel the same sense of hopelessness that he had inflicted on Bert. And he needed to set it up in some way that he could be sure he would succeed. He had plenty of time to think as he healed. Then he visited a technomancer friend of his and they put their heads together.

A week or so later, Bert showed up late one night at the Sultry Siren with his saxophone in hand. He

Jaime Lombardo & Ron Hill

had planned it so that Marcus and Sally were the only ones there when he arrived. When he saw Bert, Marcus at first had a good laugh, then became coldly menacing. He commanded Sally to stay put and stay silent, then advanced on Bert. As Marcus approached, Bert put his instrument to his lips and began to blow a soulful tune. Marcus, surprised at this reaction, hesitated a moment, then began to advance on Bert again. Rather, he tried to advance on Bert. He found that couldn't move.

As the *control mind* spell charged into the saxophone took effect, Marcus found that he could no longer move of his own volition. He was totally under Bert Capricus' control. Bert knew that he and Sally could have no future as long as Marcus were around, and figured he'd be doing everyone a favor by ridding the world of a bloodsucking Vampire, anyway. So he pulled out the wooden stake he had placed inside his jacket and tossed it to Marcus. Then he played a few bars of a frenetic and staccato tune, and commanded Marcus to stake himself.

Marcus Kingston had no choice but to obey. He fought against Bert's control, but to no avail, and drove the stake through his own heart, uttering a soul-rending shriek as he collapsed face down onto the stage. With Marcus destroyed, Sally was able to react again. Unfortunately, she was still feeling the effects of Marcus' influence. She saw what had happened to her "love" and broke down. In her grief-stricken state she could not think before acting and threw herself onto the body of Marcus Kingston, impaling herself on the stake that protruded from his back.

At that, Bert Capricus snapped. He fell sobbing at Sally's side. After what seemed like an eternity, he climbed to his feet and looked down at his handiwork. He hurled the saxophone into the band-stand, and set about to erase the entire scene from his memory. That night the Sultry Siren burned to the ground, and Marcus Kingston and Sally Sutherland were never seen again.

Bert Capricus remained a broken man. He could often be seen wandering the streets of Darnish and The Pit, wild-eyed and muttering to himself. Occasionally, the soulful notes of a saxophone could be heard coming from the banks of the Steep River. A few months after the Siren burned down, Bert flung himself into the very same river and disappeared from the sight of man. Neither he nor his sax were ever seen again.

A pretty sad story, hmmm? A tale of love found and lost, of jealousy, greed, and the price to be paid for them. How about a cup of java? Then we can get on to the next order of business.

THE SEARCH FOR THE SAX

What a sympathetic guy that Horvath is. But I'll tell ya, that legend of the charming sax is true — and Marcus Kingston *was* a Vampire. I should know, I've lived it.

I first got involved two days into the case. I was in the paper's morgue, researching some old stories, when I ran into this private gumshoe I knew. Seems he had been hired by some dame to find some of her hubby's lost property. Hubby was a musician whose career had stalled. Before he could get it back on track, he had an unscheduled meeting with the fender of a cab.

Times were bad enough that he had to hock his instrument — he played saxophone — but now wifey wanted to get it back, for sentimental reasons. At least she thought he hocked it. He may have loaned it to a friend. That's what she wanted

Jaime Lombardo & Ron Hill

the gumshoe for — to find out where it was and get it back for her. Yeah, it sounded a little fishy to me, too. So now this gumshoe and his partners were trying to track down hubby's last steps, and his friends. It was a slow news day, so I tagged along.

We went to a coupla his hangouts, and checked around in some pawn shops. We even checked in at the sentinel station to see if we could get a lead on the cabbie that hit him. Maybe he saw something that would help. Funny thing, though; the more we dug into it, the stranger it became (go figure!). It seemed that there was no accident report on file, and not many people remembered hubby. Just when it was lookin' like there were no goods to track down, we stumbled onto something.

One of the last pawn shops we were casing did have a box of property they were holdin' for some guy matching the description of our boy. It turned out, though, that the shopkeeper had already sold off the saxophone. We got the info on the joe who had walked off with the instrument, and got the rest of the property out of hock. We were on our way back to my gumshoe friend's digs to contact the grieving widow when we were set upon by a couple of goons. They weren't talkin', so we didn't know why we were on the receiving end of their antisocial behavior. We put up a good fight, but the muscle managed to walk off with the box of goods.

When we got back to the gumshoe's office, the client was waiting there. She wanted an update, so we let her know what had transpired. She didn't seem too perturbed by what had happened But when we gave the good news — that at least the saxophone wasn't in the box and we still had a shot at it — she seemed to become a little nervous. Telling her we had a lead to follow up, we showed

her out and then headed off to talk to the sap who had picked up the sax.

Arriving at the address, we were just about to knock when we noticed the door was ajar. Stepping in, we saw the tenant, the guy we were looking for, slumped on the floor. Standing over him were three big guys with a large duffel bag. We recognized them as some of the guys who had jumped us at the pawn shop, just as they recognized us. We managed to drive them off, and retrieve the bag, which contained the saxophone. Checking the tenant, we found the poor guy was dead.

Back at the office, we contacted the client. She showed up, thanked us profusely, and settled her account. By now, though, we were sort of suspicious about what was going on, so we tailed the dame. She hightailed it from the office to a warehouse in Karas. Following her in, we watched as she turned the sax over to a drop-dead gorgeous dame who moved like satin on satin. Just as we were getting ready to make a move, we heard the distinctive sound of Annie gun bolts being drawn behind us. It was that same muscle again — we were gettin' sick of their ugly mugs by now.

They brought us out to the two dames, where we found out what the scoop was. The warehouse babe was a Vampire, and "wifey" there was her front.

ADVENTURE NOTES: FINDING THE SAX

It is best when running this adventure to make sure the characters have not heard the legend of Capricus' saxophone before they get involved in the case. Otherwise, it will give away too much at the beginning. Start the adventure off as a simple missing property case, then let the progression of events start raising the suspicions of the characters. They investigating team can eventually discover the legend of Bert, Sally and Marcus later in the adventure, as they are closing in on their target, if they discover it at all.

The Vampire at the end of the adventure does not have to be physically dispatched. You may want to have her escape, so that she can bedevil the characters at a later time. They've annoyed her and thwarted her plans, so she becomes an ongoing nemesis for the team.

Likewise, the saxophone itself does not have to go missing. Perhaps the team manages to hold on to it. Then they can use it, sell it, or do whatever. Or it can be destroyed somehow, so that no one has the power anymore, and it won't show up again.

The whole scam was run to find the saxophone for Vampy. Turns out it was magically charged. As we discovered, it was the saxophone of Bert Capricus.

Seems the spells on the sax make it able to charm Vampires, when it's played by a Human. What Vampy had discovered was that it could charm Humans as effectively when played by a Vampire, which is why she wanted to get her hands on it (yeah, it's a charming instrument, all right). And apparently, she was tight with Marcus Kingston when he was "alive," and so wanted to avenge his destruction in some way. Needless to say, we got involved in a knock-down drag-out fight and managed to finally dispatch the bad guys. Unfortunately, in all the ruckus the sax went missing again. One of these days we'll track it down again, if no one gets to it before us.

THE CAPRICUS SAX

The saxophone itself is a regular, nondescript musical instrument, looking much like any other saxophone. However, it has charged into it a potent *control mind* spell, which is activated when the instrument is played.

The user must target the spell, either by looking at the target or playing it in the direction of the target, and then play a few notes on the saxophone to release the spell. The target must be within 10 meters of the caster. Successfully playing a few notes requires a Mind or *artist: musician* roll against a difficulty number of 8.

If the saxophone is successfully played, the *control mind* spell is triggered. The effect value of the spell is 20; compare this to the target's *willpower* or Confidence. If the spell is successful, the caster has taken control of the target's mind. The duration of the control depends on how well the spell succeeded. Consulting the Success Chart, read across from the number of result points in the first column to determine the level of "General Success." The results are summarized in the following chart.

CONTROL MINDS SUCCESS CHART

Success Level	Duration
Minimal	The effect lasts for a minute
Solid	The effect lasts for two minutes.
Good	The effect lasts for three minutes.
Superior	The effect lasts for five minutes.
Spectacular	The effect lasts for ten minutes.

In that time, the ensorcelled character will do whatever the caster requests, as long as it is not life-threatening. If the request is to do something completely against the target's nature (murder someone, for example), the target gets to make a *willpower* or Confidence roll to resist, with an automatic +5 to the total. If the request is to do something that actually threatens the life of the target, the target also gets to make *willpower* or Confidence roll, once again against the effect value of the spell and receives an automatic +10 to his total. If the target succeeds, he has broken free of the effects of the spell altogether. Otherwise, he must continue to obey until the spell wears off, even to the point of killing himself.

The particular version of the *control mind* spell charged into the saxophone, however, is only effective against Vampires (Bert was rather single-minded in his pursuit of vengeance). In addition, due to a magical fluke during its creation, the spell has a peculiar side-effect. It *is* effective against Humans, but only if the user of the saxophone is a Vampire. Bert was not aware of this for the short time he owned the instrument, and it is still a fact known only by a very few who have come into contact with the sax.

The saxophone was originally imbued with five charges of the *control mind* spell; it currently retains three of those charges.

A GENTLEMAN'S DEMON

… So you see why it is highly unlikely that there was a Vampire in our fair town, hmmm? These sorts of things just don't happen around here. Believe me, I would know if they did.

Now, that is not to say that nothing Unnatural ever makes it inside the walls. The Wilderness Squads are very effective in their jobs, but every once in a while something particularly clever manages to come in from the Wilderness — or beyond. I can tell you with certainty that we have had our share of Demons over the years; Relkazar are the worst, and then there are those disgusting little Sketh.

But here's something I'd be willing to wager you didn't know. You think of Relkazar and you think of ravening Demon hordes, and of a massively-built creature who would as soon rend you limb from limb as give you the time of day. Assuming, that is, that it didn't covet your body and possess it, consigning you to oblivion in the process, hmmm?

However, not all Relkazar are the Chaotic creatures of legend. Some of them are very willing to deal with Humans (and others) on an equal footing. So the next time you encounter one of them, give it a chance and talk to it first … but from a safe distance.

AN UNNATURAL ENCOUNTER

The night was cold and dreary, and seemed even worse than it was to Elacar Stang, mainly because he had been standing out in the chill drizzle for a little more than three hours. But his information was accurate — it had better be, or that little weasel that sold it to him would get a taste of just how miserable it felt to be standing out in the cold night air with nothing to show for it.

Stang snapped out of his reverie when he noticed a light go on behind one of the shuttered windows on the ground floor. At last, someone was about in the place. He slipped from concealment and made his way quickly across the street.

He had already cased the joint and knew how he was going to get in. The simple lock on the side door gave in easily to the pick he slipped into it, its wards crumbling in the face of the counterspell focused into his lockpick.

Opening the door just wide enough, he seemingly vanished into the dark interior. Once inside, he padded quietly to the door, listened a moment, then exited into the equally dark corridor. He made his way down the hall to the room where the glowstone had flared into life and placed his hand on the doorknob.

At that moment, as if a veil had suddenly been lifted from his mind, he sensed that something … *Unnatural* … was very near. Reflexively, his claws extruded from his fingertips. His hand clenched tightly around the knob for a split second, then he thrust the door open and leaped into the room with a barely stifled growl. Before him towered the form of a Demon, its ebon wings at full spread practically filling the room. The Demon's great horned head lowered its gaze to Stang, and the dark maw parted to reveal dripping, glistening fangs.

"I say, Mr. Stang, there's no need to be so melodramatic, don't you agree? Do sit down and we'll chat a bit."

A NOT-SO-EVIL "TWIN"

Ol' Sammy's on the right track, but once again the finer niceties elude him. There are Demons whose first thought is not to off you if you look at 'em wrong. But they ain't Relkazar. They look a lot like 'em, but their attitude is different. They're called Glevdrazar. Yeah, really. And if you got a beef with that, then talk to one o' them, not me. I'm just tellin' ya what I heard. And before you go thinkin' that the guy I heard it from is a few spells short of a grimoire, or just puttin' me on, let me tell ya that I heard it from a Glevdrazar himself.

Yeah, I actually met one of 'em. And it goes to show something that I'm here to talk to you about it. It was a strange case, I remember; me and some buddies were hot on the trail of some cultists who were planning something dastardly for the whole town. We had followed them down into the sewers, which turned out to be connected to some natural tunnels under the city. After crawlin' around in the dark for much too long, one of my pals found an opening in the wall.

Going through, we found ourselves in the basement of some kind of shop. But before we could get our bearings, and just as noticed the musky stench permeating the place, we were set upon by a crowd of Sketh. Things weren't goin' too good for us. We managed to take out a few of the little pests, but before long it looked like we were all gonna end up about as sharp as a Taxim wino.

That's when a massive voice came booming down into the room. The Sketh instantly disappeared into the nooks and crannies of the musty old place. Those of us who could still think about it probably would've preferred to take our chances with the Sketh than with whatever had just yelled out. But when the speaker came down the stairs it was some wizened old shopkeeper. That really threw us for a loop — this little guy scared off all those Sketh? His name was Silas Barstow. As he spoke to us, the Sketh slowly slinked out of their hiding places and congregated around him, but they didn't go after us again. He wanted to know how we gotten into his basement and why we were there. When we explained it, he seemed really interested — but in a theoretical way, almost, like it was some puzzle to be solved.

Anyway, it turned out that Silas was able to get us back on the right track, and give us a lead as to where we could find the cultists' secret worship chamber. All he wanted in return was for us to let him know how it turned out. He was a weird one, though. He wore these really dark sunglasses the whole time we were there, even in that dismal basement. He didn't explain why he had Sketh runnin' around his basement, and why they seemed to listen to 'im. And, get this, the shop he ran was a curio shop. Big surprise, huh?

I've dealt with this guy a few times since then. As long as I have interesting information for him, he's got info for me. He knows a lot about what's goin' on around town, especially the mystical stuff. I found out why on one of my visits. As he was rummaging through some old items in one a' his display bins, his glasses got dislodged. Brother, you never saw someone hightail it so fast to get them back on. But before

Jaime Lombardo & Ron-Hill

he could, I noticed his eyes. They were glowin'! A pale, bright blue. At first he looked like he was ready to blast me into another dimension, but he calmed down quick and got control of himself.

I finally got him to spill the beans. That's when he told me what he was — a Glevdrazar. He said his kind were more cerebral than Relkazar, with insatiable curiosities. That's why he had taken the form he had. It put him in a good position to learn a lot about what was goin' on in this world. He turned out to be an all right kinda guy, for a Demon. You just gotta watch his temper, 'cause there's always that Demon spirit underneath it all, and you never know when it'll come boilin' to the surface. Turns out he has the Sketh in the basement as his watchdemons, since he knew about the secret passage.

I still stop by every once in a while, to trade info or to shoot the breeze about Unnatural goings-on, but I haven't learned too much about the Glevdrazar. I just know that they exist and how they differ from Relkazar. Even Silas doesn't know too much about why there is a difference, or how they're related to the other Demons.

Perhaps they're from some dimension close to but not quite that of the Relkazar — that might explain the physical similarities — *and* the difference in viewpoint and attitude. I'm no professor of the demonic, so what do I know?

I haven't heard about these demonic joes in any other cities I'm familiar with, but given how secretive they are, that's about what I would expect. My guess is, wherever you can find Demons, you can probably find Glevdrazar.

GLEVDRAZAR

"Calm yourself. I'm not going to rend your limbs from your body, at least, as long as you don't give me

a good reason. My appearance may be intimidating, but I'm not as brutal as my 'cousin,' the Relkazar. Well, I use the term cousin loosely. No one is quite sure what the connection really is, but that's not what's important right now. You see, I'm looking for some information, and I hear you're the one who has it.

"That's right … information. Don't look so aghast. It's not like you're the only ones with a curiosity. You think you have some monopoly on thought? I'd wager that I could tell you a thing or two about this world you claim to know so much about. Just because I am physically powerful doesn't mean I have no brain, or any interests other than terrorizing Humans.

"Now you know why I prefer to take other forms. That's right. I, too, can change my form to its essence and possess the body of an intelligent being. And believe me, for most beings that would be an improvement, since I give the body an intellect much greater than the one that previously occupied it. In fact, that might be the only thing that would give me away — the fact that my host was now so much more erudite. Well, that and the glow in my eyes. But at least in a less imposing form, I am free to travel about without interference and pursue the information that most interests me.

"Oh, yes, speaking of information, I believe you were about to give me the facts I was seeking. Hurry now, or I might forget that I'm a civilized being, and your limbs will discover an independent existence after all."

The Glevdrazar is one of the creatures whose existence has remained relatively unknown. This is not so much of their own doing, as it is due to the normal reaction of Humans when encountering a Demon. Rather than noticing the slight differences between Glevdrazar and Relkazar, most people

Jaime Lombardo & Ron Hill

AGILITY 8
DEXTERITY 7
ENDURANCE 7
STRENGTH 10
TOUGHNESS 10 (16)
INTELLECT 10 (12)
MIND 10
CONFIDENCE 9
CHARISMA 8

Skill Notes: Glevdrazar concentrate on Intellect and Mind skills, and are very likely to have one or more magic skills.

Alignment: Most Glevdrazar are affiliated with Order.

Natural Tools: Wings, speed value 10; claws, damage value STR+3/18; hide, armor value TOU+6/19. Like their "cousins," the Relkazar, Glevdrazar may possess a victim and take complete control over him or her. From that point on, use the Intellect, Mind, Confidence and Charisma stats of the Glevdrazar in place of those of the victim. The victim's physical attributes do not change. The Glevdrazar will be able to use any physical skills of the victim for as long as he is in possession of the body, but none of the victim's mental skills will be available to the Demon.

While possessed by a Glevdrazar, the victim's eyes glow blue.

THE SPIRIT OF THE WILDERNESS

Oh, no, my friends, you do not want to travel into the Wilderness. Not for pleasure. When you travel to another city, you have no choice, hmmm? But now that you are here, there is plenty to do within the walls of our fair city. Sightseeing is not something you want to do on the outside.

No, exploring is even worse. Exploring the Wilderness means you are seeking something, and wish to claim it. But the Wilderness will not allow it. We here in Albredura have known this for many years. The Wilderness is conscious, and does not allow itself to be robbed. Many times have adventurers and explorers ventured out to the northern reaches and the great forest there. They have brought back artifacts and treasures, and even more mundane goods.

But each time they do, the Wilderness reclaims them. It sends forth its spirit to right the wrongs perpetrated upon it. Adventurers are found dead, or never seen again. And their treasures vanish, retrieved by the Wilderness itself. No one has ever seen it work its will upon those hapless souls, but the end results are often ghastly to behold. No, if you value your lives, do not even think of plundering the Wilderness.

will hightail it out of there just as quickly as their legs can carry them, and spout the tale of escaping from another Relkazar.

Glevdrazar are as physically imposing as their "cousin" Demons, but slightly less physically powerful. They are more intellectually involved, however, and have a great curiosity. Sometimes this is to their detriment, as they can become focused on their current interest to the exclusion of all else. Because of their more cerebral nature, they are more apt to possess magical skills, and many Glevdrazar are quite adept at different schools of magic.

Glevdrazar look much like Relkazar, but generally have shorter horns that do not curve. Although they are more inclined to matters of thought than action, they are equally as arrogant in their self-attributed superiority. Glevdrazar do not seek out positions of power, but prefer to remain on the sidelines, observing. They tend to become information brokers, working independently. If they are summoned by priests, it is usually for the knowledge they can impart, although they drive a hard bargain for that knowledge.

IF THE SPIRIT MOVES YOU, SHOVE BACK

Boy, that Wilderness drivel really has Sammy spooked, doesn't it? I tell you, though, before I stumbled onto the story, I might have given that tale some credence, too. You can't deny that expeditions that have brought things back from the Wilderness, particularly the northern forest, have met untimely ends with nothing left to show for it. That's a matter of public record. But it turns out that there is an actual explanation for what's going on.

Well, of course I'm going to tell you. I didn't go through all of that set-up just to change the subject. Well, I was working a story that was close to my editor's heart. He had me looking into the doings of a large transportation firm, Fordern's Shipping and Caravans, Inc., because he was certain that there was some gangland trouble brewing. You see, Fordern's had gang connections, and we had discovered that occasional small caravans were making unscheduled runs outside of the city. It was almost certainly some kind of smuggling operation. The questions were, what were they smuggling, and where were they smuggling from?

On top of that, each time a shipment was brought into the city, the people involved with it would disappear, or turn up as grist for a flesh mill. It was becoming a bloody mess, and we wanted to blow the lid off it. It started off like any other investigation, but soon became something much more.

The first thing I did was to tap the resources of a sentinel of my acquaintance. He was working the organized crime detail, so he had the skinny on the gangs' dealings. The only problem was, there wasn't any gang war brewing. Fordern's was indeed connected. A tortuous paper trail led right to the warded doorstep of Paracelsus Calhoun, one of the small-time "mob bosses" who had his fingers in counterfetiting and trucking companies. But there was no bad blood with any of the other gangs at this particular juncture. And none of the gangs were showing any increased revenues, like they would if they were bleeding off Calhoun's goods. So who was puttin' the hit on 'Celsus' boys?

The next thing was to find out what exactly was being smuggled into the city. That called for some good old-fashioned legwork. Unfortunately, it also meant a few nights of stale sandwiches and cold coffee staking out Fordern's joint. It paid off, though.

It was about half past one in the morning when a commotion at the side gate stirred me out of my reverie. At first I thought it was just the arrival of the trucks, but while they were still being driven in the tone of the voices changed. Here was a muffled shouting, and many insistent voices calling out

BACKGROUND NOTES: GLEVDRAZAR

Advantages/Compensations
3CIV

Mandatory A/C
Advantages: Special Abilities (CIV): Flight, Natural Armor, Natural Weaponry (HTH), Attribute Increase II (Intellect +2), Possession II

Compensations: Advantage Flaw (CIV): Ability Loss IV (they lose the use of all their Advantages except Possession II when they possess someone); Infamy (CIV): universally despised (because they are usually mistaken for Relkazar, which annoys them no end), +8 to DN of all interaction attempts against those who know what they are; Achilles' Heel (CIII): *entity* spells against them add +3 to their effect values

Recommended A/C
Advantages: They may not choose any more
Compensations: Quirk (CIII): Curiosity; they are insatiably curious, pursuing whatever catches their fancy even if it places them in harm's way

Player-character Glevdrazar may choose two CIII Compensations in exchange for one CIV, as long as they take the mandatory Compensations listed above

Restricted A/C
They are not allowed any more

sharp, quick commands. then there were gunshots, and even the occasional flare of a spell being fired off. Taking advantage of the commotion I sidled over to the front gate and wormed my way in while everyone else there was occupied by what was happening at the side gate.

Skirting the edges of the yard, I worked my way over to the office. I climbed over a pallet of crates that was stacked along the fence and dropped back to the ground and suddenly found myself face to face with the biggest, ugliest brute I have ever had the misfortune to run into in the dark. It was crouched down behind the crates, and seemed as if it had just been watching what was transpiring in the yard just before I drew its unwelcome attention. It was tall, even crouched down as it was, and slender, but still seemed massive. It was covered in long, stringy grey hair or fur.

Startled, I stepped back and reached for my camera, but while I was fumbling for it, the creature reared up, swatted me with one long arm and sent me rolling. I jumped to my feet, but the thing was gone.

Gathering my wits, I remembered why I was here, and continued on to the office. The commotion was still going strong over by the side, and was occasionally punctuated by screams and gunshots. There were a lot of expensive runeslugs being hurled about, too. I worked my way into the building and found some file cabinets in a small office near the back of the small building. As I started to rummage through the drawers, I turned up lucky, spotting a folder spread open on the desk. It looked like it dealt with the shipment just arriving.

Skimming it quickly, I got the gist of it, then snapped a couple of shots with my camera for later study. That's when I noticed that the commotion outside had subsided. I headed for the door, but too late. There were a couple of mugs just about inside already. I ducked down behind some crates. I was able to hear everything they said. The two mugs turned out to be Mr. Fordern himself and his foreman. They were discussing the unsuccessful raid on the caravan. Based on their conversation and the files I had seen, I was able to piece together some of the background.

THE LOWDOWN

It seems that Jackie Fordern had found himself a deserted temple in the Wilderness that was stocked with treasures. A local box artist on the lam had decided to try his luck making it to another city. Heading north with a coupla buddies, he was in sight of the forest when a queskworm attack broke up his little escape party. Hightailing it to the cover of the woods, he wandered about for a couple of days and eventually stumbled onto the ruins of a temple. Taking cover there, he discovered that there were quite a few hidden chambers stocked with gold, gems and artifacts. Figuring that he could buy himself safety with this find, he decided to head back to the city and arrange to have it picked up.

Somehow he made it back across the Wilderness. He must've been one lucky mug, that's for sure. Well, he came to Jackie Fordern with his story, 'cause he knew he'd need some heavy trucks to clean out the temple. A deal was struck, and for the last few weeks, small convoys were working their way back and forth, carting in the ill-gotten plunder. The problem was, somebody else wanted the loot, too. After the first load made its way back, a lot of it started disappearing. So did the people guarding it. At first Fordern thought that they were trying to bamboozle him. But then some of the bodies started turning up. Then he knew they were under assault.

With each new truckload came new attacks. I could tell from his tone of voice that he was becoming exasperated. He even seemed ready to give up on this venture. It wasn't worth the cost in property and

manpower. When they headed into a back office, I took my opening and beat it out of there quick.

It was already getting light out by the time I got back to the car. Driving back to the office, I went over things in my head. The coffee was even colder now than before, so I thought the mental exercise might help to keep me awake. Something didn't add up. Jackie Fordern's shipments were being raided so successfully that he had made nothing on the deal. In fact, he was losing quite a lot trying to hold onto what little bit he could. Yet no other mob was showing the profits. Who was hitting the shipments? And what the hell was that creature in the shipping yard? I was bumping up against a dead end, so I told myself then to let it lie for the night, even though I knew I wouldn't. It was late, and time for me to get back to the office where I belonged.

THE WRAP-UP

Just then it hit me. That's where the looted goods were going — back where they belonged. Maybe the temple ruins weren't deserted, and somewhere around that temple were the people who had built it. Of course they'd want their treasures back. And apparently they were very good at getting it back, since no one had even gotten a look at them. At least, no one who was still around to tell about it.

The question was, where were they now? They'd just hit Fordern's place, so they couldn't have gotten far. It was light now, so they couldn't travel openly. Where could they hole up until dark? Back at the offices of *The Newsmage*, I consulted a map of the city. Fordern's shipping company was located in Karas, the industrial part of town. The temple folk were going to be headed north. Tracing a line to the north side of the walls I came across Hefton Park, in Neln. A long time ago it used to be a nice place, I'd read. But then the outer city had turned to the Haunts, and no one felt comfortable visiting a natural enclave so close to the wall. The park fell into disuse and the vegetation got wild since no one kept it up. If I came from a forest and had to hide out, that's where I'd go.

So go there I did. It was getting dark by the time I arrived. Sneaking through the underbrush, I kept my eyes peeled, trying to find the camp I expected. It was very quiet, and I couldn't pick up any of the sounds I'd expect from an encampment. Then something caught my eye. On a low thorny shrub was caught a tuft of long grey fur. Just like the fur on that creature at Fordern's yard. Then I realized it. The temple folk weren't *people*, they were something else altogether. Pushing through the thorn bushes (I'd probably have to get a new suit now), I spotted them. It was an eerie sight. There must have been about 15 to 20 of them. They were

Jaime Lombardo & Ron Hill

moving about like tall thin shadows among the trees, preparing their treasure to be carried home. But there was no sound at all, except for the wind.

Grabbing my camera, I got off a couple of shots before I felt the brush moving behind me. I turned just in time to see another of those things looming above me, arms raised as if to strike. I ducked to the side and tried to run around it, but got tangled in the thorns. I managed to break free, but too late. Two huge arms came at me, and I thought about the story that might have been as a hollow darkness rose up and dragged me down …

I felt like I'd welcome the darkness again, if it was the alternative to the pounding in my head. I came to in the same thicket I had gotten caught in. Looking around, I found that the park was deserted. I ran around, checking for everything I had seen, but there was no trace that anything or anyone had ever been there. Not even a tuft of hair. The I remembered the camera. I found it in the thicket, or rather, I found the pieces of it. It was thoroughly trashed, and what I could find of the film was shredded into fine slivers. It seemed that the spirit of the Wilderness had gotten its way again. And only I knew that it wasn't the Wilderness incarnate, and its spirit was really *spirits*.

So there you have it. The inside scoop on the whole amazing tale. Unfortunately, no one ever got to read this story. It was too farfetched, even for a city on the lookout for the Unnatural, and since my camera and all other evidence was destroyed, there was no proof. So I settled back into my routine, covering the local stories, digging up the dirt on the crooks and the crooked, and trying hard not to keep looking over my shoulder every time it got dark.

CARENTHALS

One of the lesser known species residing on Marl are the Carenthals. Very is little is known of them, and very few people know of them. This is due in part to the fact that they reside in the Wilderness where few dare to go, and to the fact that they are extremely quiet and stealthy creatures.

Carenthals first came to Marl during the Godwar. After it passed, they were left here, and soon made their way into isolated areas so that they could live in solitude. Carenthals become the protectors of the areas they inhabit. They maintain their locales in the state they found it in. They are extremely Order-aligned, almost to the point of stagnation. If anything of value is taken from a location "guarded" by Carenthals, they will dispatch a few of their number to retrieve it and return it to its "rightful" place. The standard method is for one Carenthal to attempt the retrieval at a time. If one fails, another gives it a try. This will continue until they are finally successful. They will continue to dispatch new groups if necessary.

Carenthals are extremely stealthy, moving without noise, and have an uncanny knack for not being seen. If they must fight, they prefer to do so in close combat, using their claws to tear at their opponents. If they kill a foe, they will bring his body back with them when they return home. Carenthals may also hurl rocks and other natural weapons at enemies.

The average Carenthal stands about two meters tall. They are covered with a long, fine, light-grey fur, which grows everywhere but the palms of the hands, the bottom of the feet, and their faces. Their hands sport sharp claws, which are their primary weapons.

ADVENTURE NOTES: TANGLING WITH THE WILDERNESS

This adventure can be run as presented, where the characters find themselves drawn into the conflict between Wilderness looters and the Carenthal. Depending on your setup, and the characters' inclinations, they may throw in their lot with either side.

To make it even tougher on the characters, they could be ones who discover and loot a location in the Wilderness. Then they will fall victim to the sneak attacks of the Carenthal, either on the way back to the city, or after they arrive there. Maybe they make it back all right and figure they've got it made. After they get comfortable with that idea, then have the attacks begin. If they realize soon enough what's going on — maybe they uncover some inkling of the legend, or run into someone else who has lived through the same thing — they can give up the purloined treasure and allow the Carenthal to bring it back to the Wilderness. It may be disappointing, but at least they're still alive. Hey, and who said Marl was a fair world?

Another possibility is that the characters are guards for a caravan that has picked up a treasure from the Wilderness. They will not be the main target for the attacks, since the Carenthal are after the stolen property, but they will be in the line of fire. This variation on the adventure also sets up the possibility for some interesting conflicts. If the characters can figure out what it is the Carenthal are up to, they may try to persuade the caravan master to give up the loot. He will, of course, refuse, and the characters will have to decide just who deserves their help more. Just remember, they have to get back to civilization somehow.

Their heads are slightly elongated, coming to a rounded point at the top. Some fur grows on their upper lip, giving them the appearance of having a long drooping moustache. The hair on their head generally hangs down in front of their faces in scraggly strands, making it difficult to see their features. Those features are look distorted when visible, as if the face had been scarred and burned numerous times. The only smooth features on their faces are their large, round milky-white eyes.

When a Carenthal is killed, its body desiccates rapidly, leaving only a fine dust and some stray tufts of hair, which are quickly dispersed by even the slightest of breezes. Within minutes, there is no trace that the creature was ever there.

As Carenthals are solitary creatures with very one-track minds, they are not suitable as player characters.

STANDARD CARENTHAL

AGILITY 11
Acrobatics 12, climbing 14, dodge 13, running 14, stealth 15, unarmed combat 14, unarmed parry 14
DEXTERITY 8
Thrown weapons 12
ENDURANCE 9
STRENGTH 10
Lifting 13
TOUGHNESS 10 (12)
INTELLECT 10
Camouflage 12, tracking 13
MIND 9
CONFIDENCE 10
Willpower 14
CHARISMA 7
Life Points: 4–6
Alignment: Carenthal are very much inclined to Order, as they live to maintain the status quo.
Natural Tools: Claws, damage value STR+3/18; fur, armor value TOU+2/17.
Roleplaying Notes: When staging the appearances of the "Spirit" of the Wilderness, strive to play up the mystery of it. When first encountered, there should be only a single Carenthal. In fact, most encounters should be with a single Carenthal. It is possible that one of them will be killed in combat. Let the characters think they have defeated the Spirit. Then watch their expressions as it returns, once again whole. In reality, it is another Carenthal, although they will not know that since all Carenthals look alike. This can go on as long as you like, so that the characters begin to think they can never be rid their nemesis. In fact, you should not reveal that there is a whole race of these creatures, and the characters can go through many other adventures wondering if the Spirit of the Wilderness will ever return to bedevil them again.

OUR CAR IS WAITING

The next time you're in town, look me up, okay? I'll be glad to set you straight on some of the other wild stories you're apt to hear around here.

I wish you a safe trip back. Do come back and visit again, hmmm? There's still so much more to tell you about.

CHAPTER THREE

GUILDSPORT: BAY OF PERIL

Guildsport. Hunh. It's a city of small-timers; always has been. Can't seem to get outta the shadow of its founders. But that's all changing … for the better? For the worse? Wouldn't you like to know …

— Oscar Marsh, Full-time Bailiff Detective, Part-time Philosopher

HISTORY

If there's anything I've learned from being born, growing up, and living in Guildsport, it's that history – ancient history – ain't gonna tell you a thing unless you know what you're looking for. I mean, knowing the full-blown historical dope of Guildsport won't matter a damn on the docks or down Guild Row, and you'll impress only the wrong people in the Wilds.

Guildsport started out as the northernmost keep-port of the continent of Eln. It's still the northernmost city, but it's now much more than a keep. Recent history will tell you that "Northport's" government has been overthrown, and that Guildsport's run by the Guilds. Smart money says there's more to it than that, but you'll find out about that later.

ADVENTURES IN GUILDSPORT

The narrator, Oscar Marsh, is giving you his best effort at a description of the city. But he's not telling you what you might want to know most: What can a party of adventurers do in this cold northern city?

Guildsport is run by its economy, and anything that upsets that is *bad*. Adventurers might be hired to do just that — or to prevent it, or to expand it. The sidebars in this chapter provide ideas on what sort of adventures can occur in the city.

Jaime Lombardo & Ron Hill

GEOGRAPHY

Guildsport's the northernmost city on the continent of Eln. It's a port city, right at the base of the Great Bay, where the weather ain't gonna freeze you to death – most of the time. Actually, Guildsport's influence creeps up three sides of the Great Bay in the summertime, and most of the southern shore in the winter.

Yeah, my ancestors count themselves among the "conservatives" ("Death to breeds! Death to Unnaturals! Death to anything that ain't like me!" You know the spiel.) They first set up the city around Northport Keep and slowly swallowed up the land around the tip of the Great Bay. Logging and mining camps cropped up in the summer, and broke down in the winter — just like it's safer to be out in the Wilderness during the daytime than at night, it's a hell of a lot easier to keep your head attached to your shoulders in the summer than in the winter. Most Unnaturals seem to "go to work" when Humans and Breeds "go to sleep." At least, that's the dope I hear.

THE GREAT BAY

Discovered by Some Dead Guy, Many Years Ago, this sheltered northern inlet spends at least four or five months a year blocked off from the rest of the world by ice. But don't worry, the Great Bay itself doesn't freeze over — at least none of the old streetsingers or history nuts I talked to ever heard of that happening. So the winter fishing industry doesn't plunge into the red like everybody else.

By the way, someone told me once that the Great Bay used to be called "Teardrop Cove," 'cause of its shape. I don't know if that was a joke or not, but I'm glad some map-head decided to rename it when he drew the official chart. We've got too much damn slang about gangsters and stoolies "taking a dip in the Bay" without the obvious crap the other name would conjure up.

BAY POINT

Actually Guildsport's got two Bay Points — east and west. At the top of the Bay, where the ice forms in the winter, two dark towers guard the bay's narrow mouth. These are the watch-towers, built gods and devils know how many years ago to look out for ice and for other ships. No vessel can sail between them unnoticed (yeah, tell me another one) and they're staffed by Wharf Bailiffs who are masters with small sloops — they can get a "Bay Alert" to Guildsport in under eight hours. The Bay Point watchers also have radio crystals and specially made spellstones that flare into the air to alert Guildsport to dangers coming from the north.

PURE RACES IN MINE TOWN

Herruk and Grani are 'Shifters, detailed in *The Unnaturals* sourcebook. They may be pure races, they may be magespawn — nobody really knows. Grelfar, or "Burrowers," are pure races who pre-date Humans in the north. They don't play a big part in Guildsport's history, but they're there, nonetheless.

STANDARD GRELFAR (BURROWER)

AGILITY 8
DEXTERITY 9
ENDURANCE 10
STRENGTH 10
TOUGHNESS 11 (18)
INTELLECT 8
MIND 8
CONFIDENCE 8
CHARISMA 6

Skill Notes: Grelfar gain +2 to all their skill rolls while underground, and -4 to all their skill totals while aboveground.

Natural Tools: Grelfar can use their hands and feet almost interchangeably, and they have claws on both they can use for digging. These claws are STR+3/12 when used in combat. They also have exceptionally tough hides which give them TOU+7/18 armor under all conditions.

Alignment: Burrowers are usually Order-aligned, though there are probably some Oathbreakers.

Description: Grelfar are known as "Burrowers" for good reason. Built for digging and wriggling through dirt and rock, they are clever tunnelers and almost never lose their sense of direction underground. They have excellent senses of hearing and smell as well — and most have a kind of "sixth sense" that helps them detect danger underground. This "warning sense" seems to expand to include almost any danger they might encounter when they are around other species of Marl.

The Burrowers are a slow-breeding species. They encountered Humans and other Guildsportian Breeds when the latter began mining. Curious about "over-creatures" digging and sometimes living in the ground, they began to make contact. Unlike most "first contacts" with other species on Marl, this time the Humans didn't start a fight right off.

Burrowers value minerals and gems in the same way Humans do, but they also value aboveground foods (especially fruits and wine) even more. Many Burrowers work for the Miners' Guild for food, wine, and little pay — they enjoy working and living underground (unlike most of the other workers) and they have their own homes in the earth. As long as the Mining Guild respects their territory, Grelfars won't create any trouble for Guildsport.

But if you ask me, it's all just a waste of cash: there ain't been a serious attack on the Great Bay since the Blue Guild made fish filets outta that sea-beast about fifty years back.

THE INLAND REACHES

There are three Inland Reaches around Guildsport, but only two of them matter a damn. Hell, I've never even been to any of them, and I can live without the experience. But they're important to Guildsport's survival, so I guess I'm gonna have to tell you about 'em. You owe me for this, Jack.

THE NORTHERN REACH

Or "Mine Town" as it's usually called. Hills and mountains punch up along the western shore of the Great Bay — they're what keeps the winter wind from freezing the Bay itself, I suppose. They're not much to look at. I hear drifters yacking about how the southern mountains are beautiful and "snow-capped." Somehow, to a Guildsportian, "beautiful" and "snow" never make it into the same sentence.

Mine Town's just a collection of Guild-stamped mine tunnels surrounded by shanty-towns. Used to be the mines stood abandoned in the winter months while the workers retreated to the safety of the city or the keep, but that's changed now. The wealthier workers, most of the managers, and anyone with a family still moves into town if they can, but the mines stay open year 'round. Breeds and mining families live in those holes, keeping warm in the winter and making themselves rich. Or dead. I hear the claustrophobia gets solved the old-fashioned way — with picks, tongs, and knives.

They bring copper, iron, silver and some gold out of those mines. They bring a lot more to the Blue Guild, too, I hear, and there doesn't seem to be any sign of the mines drying up. I suppose if mining were easier or the people of Guildsport less conservative (read: "survival-oriented"), the mines would be finished off in a few decades. But they've been going for years, at a steady trickle, and Guildsport's

Jaime Lombardo & Ron Hill

BACKGROUND NOTES: GRELFAR

Advantages/Compensations
1CI, 1CIII, 1CIV

Mandatory A/C

Advantages: SupraNormal Knowledge (CIII): Because of their affinity with the earth, Burrowers gain +2 to all skill totals while underground; Special Abilities (CIV): Natural Weaponry (STR+3/12, hands and feet) and Natural Armor (TOU+7/18)

Compensations: Advantage Flaw (CIV): Burrowers have poor eyesight and are disoriented aboveground. They receive -4 to all sight-based *perception* checks anywhere and -4 to all skill checks while aboveground (these modifiers can be cumulative)

Recommended A/C
None

Restricted A/C
Any Advantages that indicate extensive time spent aboveground (most "Contacts" or "Cultures")

number one industry is still as strong as a Hugor.

Guildsport's got about a seventy-thirty split on population. That is, about seventy percent of us are Human (you know, normal), and the other thirty percent ain't. We don't hold much truck with the Undead here — plenty of hands to do most of the jobs in town without the necromancers getting busy — but there are a lot of Breeds and even a few pure races in Guildsport, scraping out a living any way they can.

The reason I bring it up here is because Mine Town breaks the curve. Tales I hear told say the Northern Reaches have, maybe, a 20-80 split, Humans to Unnaturals. And most of the Unnaturals there ain't even Breeds. You've got Burrowers, Mules, and Rock-Men (that's Grelfar, Herruk, and Grani, to you academic-types) in abundance there, along with your usual assortment of strong Breeds, all crowding up the place.

Most of the pure races (except for the Humans) stay in the mines year-round, and that's no surprise to me. Guildsport's not as cosmopolitan as I've heard some of the more southern cities are — many people (read: "Human" or "moron," here) give non-Humans trouble in the city. Breeds take a little less shit than the other pure races, I suppose, but it's still not the greatest for them, either. I've heard tell that most "scholars" don't count these pure races as part of Guildsport's population, since they don't actually live *in* the city. Bullshit. It's those same tax-heads I'd like to see get along without Burrower coal for a winter or build a house without a Rock-Man hewn foundation.

ADVENTURES IN LOG TOWN

Of course Log Town's got its problems, too. Mostly it's what Guildsportians call "infestation" – roving Unnaturals and Wilderness creatures who just haven't learned to stay away. In summertime, there's enough action in Log Town to draw creatures out of the Wilderness, but there's still too much going on for them to actually do anything to the anybody. But in the winter, when Log Town's population shrinks, the Unnaturals of the Wilderness try to take advantage. Here are some events the player characters might get tripped-up in:

†**A Demon Comes to Town.** Over the course of several winter nights, a few of the perimeter guards disappear from Log Town's walls. This sparks an investigation, possibly by the player characters. They suspect Wilderness creatures have begun to prey on the guards (naturally), but there's no evidence of violence or powerful magic. The characters can try to set a trap for whatever is taking the guards and, if they do, they are beset by a Witch-Rider (see *The Unnaturals*). The Witch-Rider tries to separate the group and ride them to death, one by one. Should the characters resist her, she escapes into the woods. Tracking her reveals that her trail doubles back into Log Town — one of the residents is a Witch-Rider, preying on the populace! The player characters must discover her identity before there's no one left.

†**Unrest in the Settlement.** Log Town has strict law enforcement, especially during the winter, when everyone huddles up for warmth and protection. But lately, people have been going off half-cocked and attacking each other, for no apparent reason. This has lead to severe discipline by the town's leaders, including banishment into the Wilderness for some of the worst offenders. At this point one of the player characters — or a friend of the player characters — falls into this madness. He or she either kills or maims someone, and faces banishment. The player characters must uncover the cause of this madness before the offender is exiled into the Wilderness to die. Their investigation leads them to discover Undead activity: a Shadow Spawn (see *The Unnaturals*) has been feeding off the residents' claustrophobia and cabin fever, making them fight each other for its own amusement. The Shadow Spawn must be defeated or banished to save the endangered character.

THE SOUTHERN REACH

This one's known as "Logger Town" or just "Log Town." Real inventive bunch in Guildsport, aren't we? Log Town's where Guildsport's lumber comes from — though most of it gets shipped out on southern-bound vessels as fast as it comes in. Our northern hardwoods, I'm told, are better than anything they can grown down south. I'm glad — it keeps the street urchins employed and out of my hair for eight months out of the year.

Log Town has recently grown into a small settlement. It just survived its third winter with no real trip-ups (true to the Guildsportian nature, they built the town into a small fortress before anyone even *tried* living through a winter out there), and even Breeds've started to move their families out of the city in favor of the Southern Reach.

But logging's always been a Human pursuit. I supposed Humans like the open air, even when it's cold, and they're willing to leave the more obviously profitable — but dirtier and more dangerous — mining to others, for the most part. Log Town's population break-down is about the same as Guildsport proper, but I've heard the people are a little more open-minded about who's a person and who's not.

Maybe that's because the Lumber Guild controls Log Town; not like the Northern Reach where a bunch of mining guilds crawl all over each other trying to take charge. I don't know, and I'm not here to find out. I'm just tellng you what the place is *like*.

During the too-damn-short summer, Log Town becomes the center of several mining and reforesting camps. Because of some ancient law one of our old Lord Protectors set up, the guilds can only rape the forest so much before they have to start planting saplings. I think this law was meant to put straps on how much lumber the traders could deal; you're fooling yourself if you think they were on some sort of conservation bent. To get around the law, lumberers slipped the Blue Guild a wad of cash to develop tree-fertility spells that keep Guildsport's surrounding forests lush and full — and without sacrificing wood quality.

Sorry, I probably shouldn't've said anything about sacrificing — yet …

THE EASTERN REACH

East, northeast, and southeast of Guildsport you can find the Eastern Reach. Take it from me, though, it's just one big empty. The land – and they've got hell of a lot more here than anywhere

else in Guildsport — is open and less mountainous here. If Guildsport's population had any real spine, they'd settle the place. But, no, the beef-growers just use the open plains for their stocks — and even then they box it in with physical *and* magical barriers.

It's probably just as well. In a few decades, I'm sure, when Log Town has grown into a small city and the mining camps become more hospitable settlements, someone will start a community in the Eastern Reach. But not now. The Bailiffs can barely cover Guildsport's bounds now, and I doubt Lord Reuben C'Tel will want to expand Guildsport eastward … at least not in the near future.

Oh, and did I forget to mention the obelisk? (I can't believe I did that — no, I'm lyin', I'd actually just rather forget it's even there). Well, way back in the hills — farther than even the nutjobs go — there's this tower of some black, reflective stone (looks like the hood of an old heap if you ask me) standing out all by its lonesome on the edge of the Wilderness. Weird markings run up its four sides all the way to the top where it ends in a pyramid shape, but no one knows what the hell the engraved scribbles mean. And for that matter, no one knows — or wants to know — who put the damn thing there in the first place.

But for the past couple of months, people've been hearing this garbled chanting coming from the hills around the obelisk. I heard that Lord C'Tel won't give in and send some Bailiffs out there — 'specially with all those creatures that make the place their playground. And now some flipper started a rumor that the obelisk's got something to do with this Godwar crap. That's all we need…

GUILDSPORT, THE CITY

Now that I've laid out the dope about everywhere in the North *except* Guildsport, I suppose you'd like to hear about the city itself. Fine. But I ain't going into as much detail as Mr. Aerech Platt did in his *Guildsport: A Historical Overview*. Anyone who wants to read that white-washed history, can (see *The Fifth Horseman* novel, Appendix A); it's not my style. I'll just tell you what I see in the city *today*, and you can figure things out for yourself.

POPULATION

Like I said, Guildsport's population is mostly Human. Counting the Reaches, that's about 20,000 people (yeah, I include Unnaturals as people) — not big by southern standards, but big enough for us.

Guildsport's growing. I see it every day. No, I don't mean I see people being born or arriving by

ships from the south — I go by a much better indicator: crime. Every day it gets more devious, more widespread and more organized than before. The "Grey Guild" used to come in on a slant — smuggling, vice, loansharking, and the occasional robbery — but now they just go all-out: murders, kidnappings, rapes. Even I'm starting to get worried about walking the streets late at night.

Still, Guildsport's a lot safer than most of the southern cities I've heard about — if you play by the rules. All the Guilds have their own enforcers, and the Bailiffs are charged with making sure nobody steps on anybody else's economic toes … and with seeing that Guild enforcers don't get too enthusiastic. Even the Grey Guild still chips in — they realize that any attention focused on them just ain't good for business.

The population of Guildsport seems to be gaining more than it loses. Even with the wanderlust of our youngsters — boarding southern ships for warmer climes — and the expansion of Log Town (not to mention the high winter mortality rate among the old or the frail), our new imports and births more than make up for it. I just hope we get a few more men in black on our side before things get out of hand.

OCCUPATION

Everybody who comes to Guildsport has a sob story about how there aren't any jobs in the south. That may make the Guild Masters straighten up with pride — no able hands are turned away in Guildsport — but I wish they'd take a look at the tale-bearers. Most of the southern cities' unemployed who make it here either leave, die, or end up out of work here, too. Guildsport was built on hard work and it only survives on hard work — anybody coming north and looking for a mountain of gold just ain't welcome.

Okay, maybe I'm painting too bleak a picture: Here's what *is*. There are dozens of guilds and demi-guilds in Guildsport, each overseeing its own facet of the city's trade. They've got complete control over all legal, and most illegal, economy in the city, and they keep everybody — Bailiffs included — on a short leash. If Guildsport's people are conservative, the Guild Masters are downright backward.

Lumber and Mining are the two biggest guilds, but they have less overall impact on the day-to-day operation of the city than most of the others. They only care about cutting trees and digging rocks and shipping south. The city is just a means to an end.

The Shipwrights are like that, too, but they're located inside the city, so they do care what's going on. Anything that might restrict trade south — and, therefore, affect the building and refitting of ships in the Great Bay Harbor — concerns them. A lot.

The Blue Guild governs the use and teaching of magic. Any magic. Oh, sure, a carpenter might use a veneer and preservation spell on that chair he's building, but he learned how to cast it and bought the spell from the Blue Guild — officially. In reality, his master probably taught him the spell when he was an apprentice — but the Blue Guild gets its cut before the chair hits the market. As a result, the Blue Guild has a finger in almost every pot in the city.

But mages are a devious bunch. I know a few, and they all seem to think they're part of this big, cosmic secret that they can't explain to the "uninitiated" without their brains hemorrhaging. As a result, the Blue Guild almost never takes an "official" stance on any policy that doesn't directly concern the use or regulation of magic. But when they do get interested in a vote you can count on the gibberers to lean on every other guild until they get their way.

The Trade Guilds are a collection of representatives for other guilds who keep track of north-south trade. They make sure Guildsport exports more than it imports — by a lot. They keep the southern cities interested in new products and new "finds" (usually minerals or lumber strains that Guildsportians have been using for decades), and they're always on the look-out for new southern developments they can sell to the individual city Guilds for their own profit.

The Beef Guild is a new organization. It used to be a part of the Farmers & Harvesters Guild, but somebody decided northern beef was getting too large to be handled under the F&H anymore. It's still small, but it's important. How important is a beef-grower's guild? Spend six months out of the year eating nothing but dried vegetables and fish and I'll tell you.

Well, those are the most important guilds; I'm not going to list all the different ones here. Put it this way, if you can think of a way to make money, somebody's already got it Guild-stamped and approved. If it's illegal, the Grey Guild has its hand in, and you've better feel around real careful, unless you want to pull back a stump.

In Guildsport, everybody works for somebody. Your average man-on-the-street is a stamped laborer, meaning he's got permission to work for any guild that wants him. Most have permanent or semi-permanent jobs with at least one guild, swapping during the seasons and hibernating in the winter. Because most of the guilds go into short operations, laborers count on the bonuses they get paid at the end of the fall season to get them through to spring. The bonuses are based on how much work they did during the year, how well they did it, and how badly the guilds they worked for want them to survive the winter.

Jaime Lombardo & Ron Hill

About thirty percent of Guildsport's employed (counting the Reaches) are tradesmen or merchants. They've been guild-stamped and guild-specified. That means they're at least journeymen in their crafts and can make and sell wares on their own, or work in a factory as skilled labor. Most of 'em are busy year-round, though the merchants can't sell much during the winter.

Roughly ten percent of the population fits into the "owners and masters" category. They live on big estates or in nice houses and give the orders. The real dope is that about half of them owe their positions to their grandfathers and grandmothers, not to their own skill. They get trained from birth to take over the "family business" and vote on the Guild Council, and then they go ahead and don't do squat.

But the other half of this group makes everything happen in Guildsport. They're the most devious bunch of back-stabbing, money-grubbing misers you'll ever see, but they're the people who keep Guildport in the black. They make the rules, they enforce the rules, and they break the rules when they need breaking. I don't have to like them, but they keep things moving.

CRIME

After a recent eye-opening, I'd say just about everybody takes part in some kind of crime. Unstamped labor, unspecified building, and minor smuggling are a way of life in Guildsport. The guilds make a new rule or pass a new restriction, and it creates a whole new under-business. And the Grey Guild's people aren't the only ones to figure this out.

But when we talk about crime, we're talking about the career criminal. It's one thing to build your own indoor shower or hire an unstamped laborer to add on a room, but it's a whole 'nother thing to build a hundred showers or run a moonlight construction operation.

These are the crimes the Guild Council is most concerned with. Unstamped and unspecified labor cut into the guilds' profits directly. Theft, murder, extortion — all those crimes are minor in the Guild Council's eyes when compared to trade crime.

As a result, the Grey Guild makes most of its money off trade crime, but at a price. Many Bailiffs have believed, for years, that the Grey Guild actually pays off the Guild Council with a piece of the action from smuggling, unlicensed labor, and other trade crimes — not as big a cut as the Council would normally get, but, hey, it greases the wheels. So the Guild Council only cracks down on obvious violations or those the Bailiffs can catch easily. If the Grey Council is smart and discreet, they can get away with anything ... up until the point they stop paying protection money.

But the sloop is rocking. More and more "unlicensed" crime (crime not sanctioned by the Grey Guild) enters the trade area every day. The Guild Council has started to get suspicious of its illegal counterpart, and the Bailiffs have been ordered to investigate deeper into the Grey Guild's business.

As far as other organized crimes go, Guildsport has its share. Prostitution is legal in guild-stamped brothels only (though house calls can be arranged), but many pimps and whores don't want to pay the fees or live out in the open. Darker perversions are also available, especially Downriver, although these are carefully regulated by the Grey Guild.

Organized theft, "cleaning," and sale of merchandise is becoming big business. As Guildsportians become more wealthy and have more money to burn, they have more items to be disposed of. In a small city, it's hard to get away with anything really big — unless you have a southern link and a way to get the thief and the goods out of town fast — but household raids are becoming more and more common.

Kidnapping has never been practical in Guildsport for much the same reason. There just ain't anywhere to hide. If you kidnap someone with a lot of money or power (and why would you kidnap someone who didn't have or wasn't connected to one of them?), they can get the Guild Council, the Blue Guild and the Bailiffs on your ass faster than you can blink. If you're powerful enough to hold them off, then you probably didn't need to go through a kidnapping to get your point across. The Grey Guild indulges in kidnapping among its members — or those who play too close to the fringe — but wisely stays away from that rap whenever they can.

THE PRECINCTS

The Bailiff Precincts are as good a division of Guildsport as you're likely to get. There are four true precincts: North, South, West, and Bay. From a Bailiff's point of view, there's also a "Wharf Precinct" along the southern edge of the Great Bay, from the northeastern edge of Guildsport to the northwestern side. Most non-bailiffs lump these areas in with the North or the West Precinct, unless they're involved in shipping ... or smuggling.

Bay Precinct is the largest and busiest area of the city year-round. Merchant's Row and Guild Street converge in the Bay (as the precinct is most often called), and taverns, shops, and tradesmen operate there year-round. There are some residences in Bay as well, but most are apartment buildings or small homes over or under trade shops. Wealthier merchants live elsewhere.

The Wharf Precinct, or the "Docks," are only two streets deep into the city. Very few people live

MOONLIGHT MADNESS

A certain craftsman, who will remain nameless, is in desperate need of certain valuable minerals and materials that come from the south of Eln. However, he does not have the money to pay the duty fees on these completely legal (he assures the player characters) materials. If he had the money, he would no doubt go through proper channels and obtain these items legally. He's got just enough money to arrange for the purchase and transportation of the items as far as the eastern Bay Point, where the cargo has to be picked up by someone he can trust – the adventurers.

Smuggling in Guildsport is a serious business. Most of it is done quietly, by the Grey Guild. This craftsman wants to avoid "owing" the organized crime of Guildsport anything, and he's made all the arrangements himself. All he needs is someone to pick up the supplies at the designated drop-off point.

It's a two day walk to the eastern Bay Point, where the adventurers meet the smuggler ship and pick up the supplies the craftsman needs. The supplies come in a small casket, no heavier than one person could carry in a backpack easily, and the adventurers need only bring the box to him. For this, he is willing to pay 1,000 Guildstamps (worth about the same here as 1,000 selasts would be worth in Selastos) — up to 100 now, and the balance later.

But the craftsman insists that the player characters avoid any contact with Guildsport's Bailiffs (who patrol the shores of the Great Bay for just such an occasion), and must not kill anyone (except, of course, any Wilderness creatures that attack them) — the craftsman doesn't want the deaths on his conscience. Under no circumstances should the characters open the box — there are precious materials in there that could be spilled or damaged easily.

The craftsman is, of course, lying. The casket contains a legendary artifact he desires for his craft. Though he will hide it from the adventurers, he is a necromancer — an unpopular profession in Guildsport — and he needs a Heart Stone for his experiments.

The Heart Stone can be used to create simple Undead (Zombies, skeletons, and the like) easily — it reduces the DN and Feedback of such spells by half. But there is a curse. If anyone carrying — or even within sight of — the Heart Stone kills another sapient creature, that person will be cursed with a Revenant (see *The Unnaturals*) created by the Stone out of the victim's spirit.

The opposition the characters face is three-fold: Wilderness Unnaturals, Wharf Bailiffs, and criminals (who have heard of the Heart Stone's arrival in Guildsport and want it for themselves). Unless the player characters are very sneaky and very lucky, they will probably kill somebody before this adventure is over … and that means a curse for all of them.

there, but during the spring, summer, and fall months, the Docks get crowded. Inns and taverns mix with brothels and toke-joints, and all are nestled in-between shipping houses, warehouses, and customs buildings. Wharf Precinct is devoted entirely to trade crime, leaving the policing of the actual streets and docks to Bay and North.

North Precinct's the smallest of the five. It rides up along the northern coast of the Great Bay almost up to Northport Keep, and most of the iKeep families live here. And then you've got a lot of the wealthier miners or mining families and some tradesmen who don't mind making the trip to Bay or Wharf every day. Of all the Precincts, North's probably got the most steam and magic heaps per resident.

South and West Precincts are where the big-shots live — especially South. A lot of "old money" gathers dust in the "Wilds," just outside South Precinct, and that's where the Beef Guild got its start — just east of the southern bulge. West Precinct ain't got as much loose cash all combined, but each person gets more than the ones down South. Guild Masters, Guild Lieutenants, and talented craftsmen, shippers, and traders make their homes here.

THE WILDS

South and east of the city proper sprawls a "district" known as the Wilds. It got its name years ago when it was the only part of Guildsport that was really "carved out of the Wilderness" and not just up against the Keep or the Great Bay. I guess officially, the Wilds are part of South Precinct, but they've got their own law up there.

The Wilds are where the real "Old Money" families live. See, back when Northport Keep opened up and let its citizens outside the walls for good, a few of the more powerful civilian factions kept trying to push the bounds. Finally, the Lord Protector and the C'Tel (that's the ruler of the Keep) said "go to

A WILD TIME

You sure you really want to go to the Wilds?

The Wilds are the best places in Guildsport for intrigue and mystery. The mansions are old and a lot of 'em are haunted — either by Undead or by dangerous secrets the inhabitants don't want revealed — like that one at the Gorlim Estate.

The Gorlims've been living in the Wilds since there were Wilds to live in. The first Gorlim was a lieutenant commander in Northport Keep, and he was awarded the land in the Wilds as a reward for long and diligent service. His military attitude and attention to detail made his estate safe and sound while others were still getting swallowed by the Wilderness.

This tradition has passed through the generations. The Gorlims have all served time in Northport Keep, as soldiers, military advisors, and civilian liasons. Even now, the oldest daughter of the Gorlim family, Patricia, is a supply officer in Northport Keep.

There are, or were, three other members of the Gorlim family left on the estate — Major Gorlim, the patriarch, an eighty-year old, bedridden antique on the verge of death, Marcus Gorlim, Patricia's younger brother and the Major's only grandson, and Mavis Gorlim, Patricia and Marcus' stepsister by their mother's second marriage.

The adventurers are called in to investigate a murder. Mavis is dead, and someone on the estate, or a Wilderness Unnatural that infiltrated the mansion, killed her and ripped her to shreds, right in her room. The Major wants to know who did it before he dies.

But death keeps coming. One by one, servants and aides disappear or die horribly during the adventurers' investigation. Finally, it comes down to the Major, Marcus, and two trusted aides. The clues point to an inside job (the gamemaster can make them up), but they don't finger anyone in particular.

But at this point the plot begins to unravel. Mavis was killed by Marcus, who raped her beforehand. But Marcus was consumed by evil dreams, sent magically to him by Mavis' mother's shade — now a Revenant with a soldier's skills, plaguing the household. She killed the servants and the others when she was released from bondage by the murder of her daughter. And she wanted him to kill the Major. See, after the woman's first husband died, she never remarried — her own father-in-law (the Major) fathered Mavis. When she killed herself soon after Mavis was born, he concocted the whole story of a "second husband" to cover it all up. The Revenant will do all it can to kill the Major, who will be defended by Marcus. It doesn't want to kill Marcus, because, even though he raped and killed Mavis, it doesn't blame him — he was driven mad by the dreams. But it does hope to clear the way for Patricia — the only unsoiled Gorlim left — to continue the family line and expunge the family honor.

And here comes the tragic twist: Patricia has known of her grandfather's evil duplicity for years. She was old enough to remember what happened, even though her brother wasn't. She got out of the estate early in life and has vowed never to return. She won't help or reward the investigators for uncovering this scandal but may, if approached gently, pay them to keep it quiet again. She will not mourn her grandfather's death, though she will miss Marcus if he is killed.

hell" and let them — as long as they understood they were on their lonesomes; the Keep didn't want that responsibility hanging over its head.

A few went to scope out the mines and eventually became the ancestors of today's mining barons. Some went into lumber country and got killed. A lot of nutjobs tried to tame the Wilderness, start winter plantations, and even beef farms … and most of them died, too.

But the strongest and luckiest Joes survived. They built big houses (with lots of smaller ones crowded around it) and made their workers and their families count on them for survival. Nowadays, most of those places in the Wilds house about one-tenth the number of people they were meant for … but that ten percent is a hell of a lot richer than anybody else in town.

The Wilds' people hire their own guards and patrols. The guards' job is to find anyone who doesn't look like they belong in the Wilds, beat them senseless, and kick them the skethspawn out of there. South patrols the place as well, but for different reasons. They're actually trying to uphold Guildsport law.

Heh.

THE DOCKS

Or "The Wharf" or "Wharf Street" or "Bay Street." Whoever you talk to might give you a different answer. Whole communities grow up together in

Guildsport. Families live in the homes their grandparents were born in, and many tradesmen never venture more than five blocks from their shops, which are also their homes. But the Docks are the exception to this rule.

There are three types of people who live on the Docks: flotsam, jetsam, and hangers-on. Flotsam are drifters from outside Guildsport. Not always from the south — maybe they came from the mines or Log Town after "deciding" it wasn't for them. They floated around Guild Row or the Merchants' Quarter and got banged up and kicked out for their trouble. Now, they're at the very edge of the city, hoping not to get pushed off into the bay.

Jetsam are the undesirables. They're the rejects from the city. Apprentices who couldn't cut the journeyman grade, sailors who lost their berths, and traders who didn't quite know how to cut a deal. They're desperate and, because of that, dangerous. They've still got heart in them and, if they can't prey off the flotsam, they'll find other targets.

The hangers-on are a mish-mosh of different types. They could've come from the flotsam or the jetsam, or they could be here on purpose, trying to make a living alongside the unlivable. Whores, pickpockets, small-time con artists and unstamped laborers fill out the ranks. They'll do just about anything for a note or a meal ... but most of them have their limits. At least up until now ...

DOWNRIVER

The river that empties into the bay carries a lot of scum with it. Through Shanty Town and out into the Bay, the river is like a breeding ground for Guildsport's unemployable. Maybe they never got a break, maybe they suffered from prejudice and neglect; I think they just never tried hard enough. Traders, merchants, and ship captains never take the "help wanted" signs out of their windows in Guildsport — we just ain't got enough labor to go around. Most of employers'll hire anybody who makes an effort to show up for work. The jobs might be crap, and the pay even worse, but it's got to be better than living in Downriver.

The first thing you notice about Downriver is the smell. For a river that flows out of the mountains and into the Bay, it sucks up a lot of filth. Take a deep breath and you risk your lungs. It's hard to even describe the stench — just think of years' old garbage, rotting carcasses, and shit, lots of shit.

The Bailiffs make an effort to beat the bounds around Shanty Town, dragging off anyone who looks like they need medical help, but they don't actually step foot onto the shack-lined streets. Not any more. There are dangerous people in Downriver — crazy-dangerous. They'll kill you because you look cleaner than them, and leave your corpse on the shore, or drag it off someplace and do gods and devils know what with it.

I'm told there are a lot of criminals hiding out in Downriver, in Shanty Town. Doesn't surprise me, but I'm not real worried. The only criminals who'll go there are the ones who've got no friends, no prospects, and no cash. They can't do anything from there — and their punishment is worse than anything we'd probably do to them. Banishment, the Keep dungeons, confinement in a Precinct hole ... that's all pretty mild compared to living Downriver. Murderers can't hide there, though — at least, not for long. The Blue Guild gets involved in murder cases, and our Bloodmages can track people down. And people who have to run Downriver can't afford counterspells.

MORE ADVENTURES IN GUILDSPORT

The sidebars listed in this chapter should give you some ideas of what sorts of adventures are possible in Guildsport. There are many intrigues you can get involved in, if you're crazy enough. My advice? Stay out of trouble. If you want to go messing around with breeds or criminals, or you feel the need for smuggling or Unnatural hunting, or if you just can't resist making a few quick stamps on the shady side of the docks or in Shanty Town, I'll be seeing you. Maybe not in jail, maybe not even in the Precinct ...

... But probably in the morgue.

CHAPTER FOUR

GALITIA: CITY OF SECRETS

The history of Galitia has been written, rewritten, interpreted, and reinterpreted so many times since the city's founding that not even the most naive of her citizens believes that what's taught in the schools today bears any resemblance to the truth. Only a few key events have been determined to be fairly accurate and therefore considered to be "historical landmarks," which historians use to gauge the reliability of other theories and accounts. But which ones hold the truth and which derive from propaganda, subterfuge, or misconceptions? Only a powerful chronomancer can tell you that … unless, of course, you happen to know an old man called Shel Hembert.

Many who have met Shel have dismissed him as a senile old ex-skinner whose brain has rotted away from too many years of breathing the noxious fumes in the flesh mills. How could his wild claims possibly be true? There's no way he's one of the original settlers of Galitia. He couldn't possibly be more than a thousand years old. Every mage, occultist, and Unnatural biologist who's examined him has come to the conclusion that he is obviously and unspectacularly Human.

And yet he remembers intimate details of every year of Galitia's existence? How does he know the secrets written in the diaries of Omeg and Sturn, secrets that have never been disclosed to the general populace in over 900 years?

If you believe Shel, it's because he in fact *was* the liaison between the original leaders of the city. He was the only being (living or unliving) who had access to the private meetings of both Omeg and Sturn. He has no explanation for his longevity, "mebbe all dem chemicalz haz pickled me soul" is all he'll say before he lapses into uproarious laughter.

According to Shel, he held too much inside information on Omeg, Sturn, and the first government of Galitia to be left free to influence politics (he knew enough dope to easily blackmail every Council Member, but his former bosses wanted to keep that pleasure for themselves), so he was sold as an indentured servant to the owner of Galitia's first flesh mill. He'll happily tell anyone with the slightest interest stories about the attempts on his life in the early years ("Was up to about three a day durin' electionz!") and how they tapered off as one-by-one the fat cats either died of overindulgence or were beaten by someone with more bribe money. Eventually, he was forgotten completely.

"And the mill ownerz, dey fergot me too!" One of Shel's favorite stories is how, after over 80 years working on the mill floor, he went into the foreman's office and asked how much of his debt he had paid off. "Da man lookz at the recordz and faintz dead away! Dey never planned on me livin' long enough to buy my freedom, soz dey never checked … I'd not only made enough ta buy myself, but dey owed me half da factory's annual income!" He was made a full partner, but put a financial consultant in charge of his estate and continued to work in the mill. "I seen what all da soft life duz ta men. I weren't about ta become one a dose fat boobs who can't tell dere friendz from dere enemiez. No sir!"

No one ever noted Shel's incredible streak of over 40,000 work-days without a sick-day or a vacation. Since management wants nothing to do with the workers, and turnover on the mill floor is so high, no one else was employed long enough to notice. He worked at the mill for over 800 years until it was taken over by one of the younger companies, the management of which retired him straight away. He had by that time accumulated an amazing fortune, but had disassociated himself from it (if anyone were to go far enough back in the records they would find that Shel owns at least a small piece of almost every long-standing business or institution in Galitia). He lives off an annuity sent by his advisors, and stays in the same dilapidated neighborhood he has lived in for nearly a thousand years.

Whether or not Shel is the genuine article or simply another deranged ex-skinner is left to the gamemaster to decide (and explain). Either way, he makes an interesting addition to a campaign. His knowledge of Galitian history is 100 percent accurate (especially when it differs from the official "truth") throwing shadows onto the question of whether he is a loopy old man or an actual survivor of the Godwar. Anyone who takes any interest in Shel and his life will find him a warm, if somewhat low-class, friend, and will be treated to a constant stream of stories about "the old days." But anyone who simply tries to use him for his information will be scorned and purposely misled.

A good portion of the information compiled for this chapter came from history books, ancient diaries, and old wives' tales, but the most important and least known knowledge passed from Shel's lips directly to these pages.

SHEL HEMBERT

AGILITY 7
DEXTERITY 7
ENDURANCE 9
STRENGTH 7
TOUGHNESS 9
INTELLECT 10
Deduction 12, first aid 11, perception 13
MIND 8
Language: (gamemaster's choice) 10, scholar: history of Galitia 15, scholar: history of Marl 13

CONFIDENCE 10
Streetwise 12, survival: urban 14, willpower 11
CHARISMA 9
Charm 10, persuasion 12
Life Points: 9

Roleplaying Notes: After living over 1000 years, Shel has developed some quirks and eccentricities (whatever the gamemaster feels is appropriate). Talking to him should be like a trip through

Tim Bobko

the Wilderness, you *never* know what will come up next. He is a crotchety old man who gives no hint of his extraordinary life's story. Sometimes he will be friendly and outgoing, other times he will be irritable and reclusive. If the characters manage to gain his trust, however, he will be a true friend and will always make time to give them his recollections on any subject.

LITTLE KNOWN FACTS OF HISTORY OR JUST 'CAUSE YA READ IT, DON'T MAKE IT SO!

STAARL, CORNERSTONE OF THE UNDEAD

One landmark event in Galitia's history is the period of "corpse riots" that occurred during the first year or so of the city's founding.

After the construction of the First Wall, the Undead in Galitia were segregated in a ghetto on the south side of town. Those that could work, for the most part held jobs either in these Undead neighborhoods or in the flesh mill. Tensions rose when the Undead population began decreasing at a steady rate directly proportional to the increase in output at the flesh mill. When it was discovered that the use of Undead workers as raw material was not only condoned by but actually originated from one of the city's founders, Omeg, the ghetto erupted in violence that threatened to spill over into the rest of the city. At this point, Omeg moved in his troops to quell the uprising and "put these afronts to nature in their proper place."

This much the historians agree on and, in fact, it is a fair assessment of the actual events. But the historians also believe that Omeg led his forces to a quick and decisive victory over the Undead — and that part of the story couldn't be further off the mark.

In truth, the corpse riots were not the unbridled chaos that they appeared to be. They had been carefully planned and orchestrated months in advance by an entity called Staarl.

It was never satisfactorily determined what manner of Undead Staarl was. His form was clearly that of a reanimated Human (with the right half of his skull caved in from the blow that took his life), but he displayed more vigor, intelligence, and free will than any of the known reanimates. Rumors at the time cast him as everything from a one-in-a-million Plague Zombie to a Shadow Spawn that had somehow survived his host's demise. Whatever he was, Staarl was the uncontested ruler of the Undead side of town. He commanded the absolute loyalty of every skeleton, Vampire, and Wraith in Galitia.

Staarl saw the plans of the "warm bodies" taking form before the thoughts ever coalesced in Omeg's mind. He knew that the living would seek to raise up their city on the bodies (and parts thereof) of the Undead, and he refused to let that happen. His plan called for the residents of the ghetto to rise up in a protest violent enough to draw the Human's notice, but not so terrible as to give away the organization supporting it.

When Omeg's troops marched in to put down the apparent riot they were surrounded and attacked by members of Omeg's own former Undead army. The Humans were routed and driven from the ghetto to deliver a message to their commander: "The Undead will not put up with your planned exploitation. We helped build this city and we will not be buried by it. Either treat us fairly, as partners in this endeavor, or it is you who will be rounded up and exterminated."

Omeg realized that if word of the situation reached the general populace Galitia would fall into anarchy (or at the very least he would lose his position as half-ruler of the city). With his forces demoralized from the beating they had taken at the

Tim Bobko

ADVENTURE HOOKS

Who, or more importantly, what was Staarl? One of the original plague zombies? A corpse animated by demonic possession? Some unknown form of 'Shifter? Is he still alive (as alive as an Undead can be) in the cornerstone of a crumbling flesh mill somewhere in the oldest of the city's neighborhoods? And where is the building? Is it still standing or has it been torn down (and if so, what happened to the cornerstone)? And is this tale even true?

Perhaps it's just another case of rumors and myths continually twisted and corrupted until they fit nicely into history. Do not look to me for answers. These questions have haunted me long enough, and I now pass the nightmares along to you, the gamemaster. But no matter what truths manifest in your mind, there are plenty of possible adventures awaiting in this little, until-now buried fact of history. To get you started down the right path, I offer one of many as yet unsolved mysteries:

The Undead of Galitia have zealously guarded the facts about Staarl's existence for a thousand years, passing the secrets from one to another, generation to generation. And during all that time not one had discovered the site of the cornerstone — until now.

The city's skeletons, ghosts, Vampires, Wraiths, and Keyth plan to free their ancient leader as soon as inhumanly possible. But how will they go about shattering the cornerstone of a centuries-old building? Do they even have the right building? And once awakened will Staarl lead the Undead in a bloodfeud against the living?

A mysterious client offers the characters a great deal of cash to recover a treasure trapped in a cement cornerstone. Why does he or she want Staarl freed? And who would refer to a homicidal zombie as a treasure? Will the characters do their own research before trying to dig out this "treasure," or will they turn the demon loose on their city filled with nearly a millenium's festering hatred?

hands of the Undead army, and with time working against him, Omeg agreed to meet Staarl in an abandoned warehouse on the edge of the ghetto to negotiate a settlement.

Of course Omeg left orders with his personal guard to hang around in the shadows until the meeting had lasted 15 minutes. At a signal from him, they were to burst in and destroy the enemy's leaders. When Omeg gave the signal, however, his guard came out of hiding straight into a crossfire. As the leader of Galitia watched, his finest troops fell dead, slaughtered by shambling hulks of near-mindless flesh. Staarl, a stinking Undead, had outmaneuvered him, and the Undead horde was now descending upon him with bloodlust in their otherwise-empty eyes.

Suddenly, with a greenish flash of magical energy, the building filled with a thick, gritty grey substance. Without a second thought Omeg dove through a nearby window, tumbling to the sidewalk below. Staarl and his Undead lieutenants, stiff-legged and slow, struggled to get out of the building, heedless of any limbs that tore free as they scrambled for the exits. And then came the second magical flash, and the strange substance that had expanded out of nothingness hardened instantly, leaving the greatest threat to the new city trapped in a cold block of stone.

Outside Omeg found his partner, Sturn, the other co-ruler of Galitia, along with several watermages and earthmages still casting at the warehouse. The two leaders argued nose to nose for a while, Omeg accusing Sturn of having his mages spy on the military and Sturn pointing out that, without his mages, Omeg would be applying for a position in Staarl's army of Undead. In the end the men agreed that Galitia needed both approaches to survive, and promised to work together more closely from this point on.

With their leader gone, the rest of the Undead fell as easily as the history books tell, and order was restored to the city just as every schoolchild learns. The block of cement became the cornerstone of Galitia's second flesh mill, an ironic end to the Undead movement, as the mill's fires burned brightly night and day processing the bodies of Staarl's people.

MIDSUMMER'S MARCH

Though everyone talks about it and thousands of people observe it, no one will admit to attending ... the Midsummer's March.

The March is a parade through the streets of Vrenthar, one of the finest neighborhoods in Galitia. Since the residents of the district remain adamant about maintaining peace and quiet (more disturbing the peace complaints are filed in Vrenthar than in the rest of the city's districts combined), allowing the parade in the first place seems odd enough. But what makes it down right unbelievable is the fact that the marchers all participate in the nude.

Rumors have it that the event began during the first summer of Vrenthar's existence. The story goes that one of the more influential members of the

ADVENTURE HOOKS

Okay, okay. I get it. You think Midsummer's March is more of an interesting background than an actual adventure setting. But are you willing to stake your soul on it? Read along before you make your decision ...

First, you need to get the characters into the March. Maybe they take a job that brings them into Vrenthar on Midsummer's Eve. Or perhaps, one of the characters receives an invitation sprayed with intoxicating perfume that requests his presence at an affluent manor house in the middle of the district. And some characters might even want to partake in the ritual without prodding from the gamemaster.

Once they're there, the fun begins ...

While in the crowd to observe the march, the characters become overwhelmed with an urge to disrobe and join the revelers. Though completely cognizant of their actions, they can do nothing to stop themselves. They parade around for several hours, drinking anything handed to them, treating naked strangers like life-long friends, and having the time of their lives. When they pass the spot where they left their clothes, they simply leave the marchers, get dressed, and go home. The next morning they awake with perfect memories of their actions, but no explanation for them. Does the Midsummer's March conceal some sinister secret? Were the charac-

ters, and all the other participants, victims of some kind of Chaotic magic or demonic possession? Or is the uninhibited atmosphere of the festival just naturally infectious?

Or perhaps the characters become involved in the March only peripherally. A wealthy client hires the characters to investigate the disappearance of her young niece. According to the client, the 17-year-old was last seen at the Midsummer's March. Of course, finding anyone to confirm this proves almost impossible (remember, almost no one admits to having attended the event and the residents all deny having seen anything at all untoward, let alone streets full of naked strangers from the poorer districts). How will they ever get a lead on her whereabouts? Will they discover the centuries-old rumor that the March serves as the cover for the activities of an ancient blood cult? Some rumors suggest that the cult must sacrifice a "wanton harlot" on the night of the summer solstice. Did the client's niece play that role during this year's ritual? And just who was the man who started the March in the first place? Does he still lurk about the streets of Vrenthar in new guise?

I'm sure your imagination has set to burning with ideas by now. Have fun, and plot with deadly abandon.

community had brought a "woman of questionable morals" home for his entertainment. The man, however, had chosen his companion poorly. The young woman had taken some form of chemical stimulant before arriving and had a serious reaction to the aphrodisiac that he had secretly added to her wine. She stripped off her clothes and began singing a popular tune as she walked out of the house and down the street. The influential resident, heavily intoxicated himself, took off his own clothes and ran after her, ordering all his servants to do the same.

Complaints flew in to the sentinels and the gentleman in question soon found himself, his partner, and all his employees in a jail cell for the night. The next morning, after paying a fine for indecent exposure (and quadrupling the amount so that all paperwork on the incident would be "misplaced") he returned to his residence in Vrenthar. He spent the next week visiting his neighbors one by one. Although none of them ever publicly discussed what happened during these meetings, the diaries of a resident (published more than 50 years after the incident) gave this account:

[He] walked in without being invited, barging past me at the door. When he got to the living room he stood facing our mantle with his hands behind his back, seeming to study the portraits of the family members and our ancestors. "Sit down" he said in a growl so guttural that it was barely recognizeable as speech.

When the entire family, even poor little Phoebe, was seated nervously behind him [he] turned to face us. As one, we let out a loud gasp. While his form was that of the man we'd known and worked with during the building of our new home and neighborhood, his countenance was that of a howling demon. And his eyes ... oh, his eyes were barely visible slits of black in pools of sickly, luminous yellow. I tell you, his eyes were glowing with the fires of hell. We were frozen in our seats, though whether this was due to a spell he had cast on us or simply our own bone-numbing fear I cannot say.

"Vrenthar is mine," he said. "I planned it. I organized its construction. I bribed the Elders to ensure our privacy. And after I brought in all the truly worthy families I knew, I was magnanimous

enough to invite others, families with potential ... families like yours, to join us. And this is the thanks I get?!?

"Listen to me and remember what I tell you ... you are all here at my sufferance! Vrenthar is mine! I will do anything I please and you will do nothing to oppose me. If I want to paint my property blood red, I expect you to tell me how lovely it looks. If I want to open a flesh mill in my basement, I expect you to tell me how sweet it smells. And if I want to walk naked through the streets in the company of whores, I expect you to either watch in reverent awe or strip off your own clothes and join us!

"But if any of you have the temerity to complain about my lifestyle or dare to ever summon the sentinels against me again, I will personally turn your life to ashes. I will ruin your lives and then I will take them. Mark my words, you would have to move to the Wilderness to find a more threatening neighbor!"

The account of what happened next springs from rumor and gossip, and has absolutely no corroborating evidence, but every scholar treats it as the absolute truth. One midsummer's eve the same gentleman again walked out of his door with a lady of the evening at his side, both of them naked as the day they were born. As he walked through the streets he blew loud and long on a trumpet (adding disturbing the peace to his other offense). But as he passed certain houses he was joined by other members of the community (we can only assume they were members of the "truly worthy families" alluded to in the diary) in identical states of exposure. The group paraded all over Vrenthar for hours, blowing horns, singing bawdy songs, and occasionally engaging in sexual acts designated as illegal to perform in private, let alone on the neighbor's lawn. They did their best to disturb and shock the non-participants and, for the most part, succeeded. Still, not one complaint was registered with the sentinels.

Perhaps the reason for this can be found in the closing passage from the earlier diary entry:

As quickly as he had appeared [he] left the house. My wife urged me to call the authorities. "He's mad as a skinner!" she said, but I barely heard her. I was staring at the spot where mere seconds earlier [he] had stood. The carpeting by the mantle, which we had paid 500 vens to have an inflammability spell cast on, had been burned through to the hardwood floor, and the wood beneath was singed black in a pattern exactly matching the position of [his] feet while he delivered his rambling threats.

We decided not to call the sentinels and, in fact, to never speak of the incident again!

Gossip about the "Midsummer Night's March," as it was called in the papers, went on for months.

Tim Bobko

Rumors and wild speculations about who participated in, organized and protected the event did not begin to die off until the one year anniversary rolled around. No further disturbances had occurred or had been threatened, so everyone wrote off the parade as a lark. It involved only the elite who felt the need to thumb their noses in the face of propriety, to celebrate the freedom and control they had won by having Vrenthar zoned exactly the way they wished.

The second march again took the population by surprise. Usually, Vrenthar was the most staid and uneventful of all of Galitia's wards. But the most remarkable aspect of the parade occurred shortly afterward. Despite the fact that the march had drawn visitors from all over the city (including reporters and photomancers representing four major newspapers and magazines), no one took a single picture or could recall even one marcher by name or face. More than 200 affluent residents of Vrenthar walked naked past at least 500 witnesses, and no one claimed to have seen anything.

Considering how the Midsummer's March had captured the public's imagination, few citizens doubted that it would become a tradition, an annual ritual that would last long after the original participants and motives had faded from memory.

Today the march has come to symbolize free expression and the power of the individual. Every year more and more marchers come from farther and farther away. Last year boasted an estimated 3,000 participants, approximately 200 of which traveled to the city from as far away as Guildsport for the sole purpose of joining the procession. And although this event has taken place in the same place at the same time every year for 250 years, and in spite of the fact that during that time more than 500,000 people have bared all in the streets of Vrenthar, no matter how many writers, artists, photomancers and law enforcement officials have attended, not one participant has ever been identified.

RESTMAN'S FOLLY

The construction of the Third Wall was handled exclusively by a private contractor named Filandrum Restman. Every surveyor, engineer, brick-layer, and earthmage who worked on the project was employed by Restman, a man who believed that beneath a tract of land that the new wall would cover rested a massive deposit of natural glowstones and other precious minerals and crystals. He paid a small fortune to obtain exclusive construction rights, with the stipulation that any natural resources found on the site would belong to him and his heirs. This agreement seemed so foolhardy that the newspapers of the time re-

Tim Bobko

ADVENTURE HOOKS

The story of Restman's Folly seems to have ended, so where do the adventures come in? Well, where did those underground structure (and the materials found therein) come from? Who built it? Why was it abandoned? And why have there never been any similar structures found anywhere else? Why did Filandrum Restman think he would find glowstones in the area? Did he subconsciously know about or feel the presence of the secret passage?

A small building in Frenzy collapses into the earth. Investigators say that an underground structure similar to the one at Restman's Folly suddenly appeared under the building, dematerializing parts of the foundation. Sentinel mages announce that evidence suggests the structure arrived through a gate, but it marks the first incident in which a gate formed in solid ground. The mages add that the gate appears to be two-way and is still active. The building's owners, convinced that great riches await on the other side of the gate, hire the characters to go through. They offer 50% of anything the character's bring back. Rumors noting the connection between this appearance and the discovery of Restman's Folly, tear through the city. How many other structures have been Gated beneath the city already, and when and where will the next one show up?

During the demolition of an old building in Das, a construction crew discovers dozens of unprocessed gold nuggets. The city's experts find deposits of diamonds and antimony in seperate locations, but there is no record of the presence of either of these minerals in the area. A "gold rush" ensues ... soon people from all over the city (and even from other cities) begin tearing up the streets of Das searching for the next vein. The characters may become involved as prospectors or as investigators trying to stop the destruction of a vital part of Galitia.

ferred to it as "Restman's Folly."

As construction continued, Restman brought in jewelers and alchemists at least once a week to assess the quality of materials unearthed during the building. For months this went on, with each batch of samples being declared "unremarkable" and work continuing as planned. And then, with the wall only weeks from completion, news of a

discovery spread across the city. Restman had found glowstones at the far end of the structure. Five independent auditors came to the same conclusion: the stones were genuine, and as per the agreement with the city, the land they came from now belonged to the Restmans.

Although the Council of Elders clung to every statute and regulation that bore even the slightest resemblance to the situation, the contract between the city and Filandrum Restman was quite specific. It didn't matter that Galitia's newest communities had already been zoned. It didn't matter that construction of housing had already begun in several areas. It didn't matter that the wall was only a few weeks from completion. The property undeniably belonged to Restman. His "folly" had paid off, and he was free to do with the land as he wished.

In considering his options, Restman came to the conclusion that he had two choices. He could begin to exploit his new land for its mineral wealth, and go through the time and expense of hiring mining engineers, miners, processors, accountants, alchemists and, perhaps most important of all, guards to defend the property from claim-jumpers. On the other hand, he could just sell the property back to the city of Galitia for a fair profit, and leave all the headaches to the Council of Elders.

Within a week he had settled on the second option and, after an arduous series of negotiations, sold all the land back to the city for just under 15 million vens. His hunch had paid off. All the public derision was just as publicly retracted and he was called "the genius of our time" ... for about three days.

As the municipal crews began testing areas for mining shafts, the ground where the first stones turned up suddenly collapsed. No one was seriously injured, but the rescued men returned with word of a strange discovery: they had fallen into an artificial structure filled with glowstones, diamonds, and currency from all over Marl. Fingers immediately pointed at Restman, insinuating that he must have had the structure built and stocked in secret to help him scam the city out of millions. The citizens of Galitia felt betrayed by the man they had charged with the protection of their families, and they cried for his death. In less than 72 hours, he was arrested, tried, convicted, and hung by the neck.

But several weeks later when the experts finished examining the site, they announced that the rooms (for there were actually five of them) and their contents had all been sealed up more than 700 years ago. The coins bore ancient insignias, and the gems and ores had been mined nearly a century ago. Restman, it turned out, was neither the genius nor the cheat he had been recently portrayed as, but rather the patsy the papers had pegged him as months earlier. He had bet his life's savings on a hunch and lost his life itself because of a coincidence.

The experts could not identify the builders of the underground structures. Several wild theories cropped up, many of which linked the rooms to the First Godwar, but the official slant on the subject is that they are "of undetermined origin." In an effort to compensate for Filandrum's death, the city turned over the contents of the rooms to the Restman family, since the 15 million vens had already been seized. The structures themselves were collapsed, and construction of Das, the Seers' Quarter, and "Frenzy" continued as originally planned.

People still tell the story of Restman's Folly to young Galitians, but the lessons gleaned from it vary from family to family. Some say the tale advises following your dream no matter how odd it seems. Others believe it teaches the rule "alchemy ain't a science, and limestone don't pay the bills."

THE MYSTERY OF ADU HOUSE

There is a building in the Seers' Quarter, very near the river, which has stood for as long as the neighborhood has been there. Adu House is its name, and it is a short, unobtrusive building. Most people walk by it without even noticing, but it houses one of the most enduring mysteries of Galitia.

Adu House is a mystery unto itself. There are no records pertaining to its construction or original ownership. It was anonymously donated to Tamborlain College (a small, but reputable educational institution where alchemists are trained) about 100 years ago. The college, for its part, pays the taxes and maintains the building, but does not use it in any official context. Originally they had planned to convert it into a library and research complex, but abruptly cancelled those plans the day before construction was to begin. The excuse given was that a carving was found in one of the walls which was "of historic nature and required further investigation." Independent analysts confirmed that the carving, found on one of the structure's support columns, had been made at the time of the building's construction, approximately 500 years earlier. However, the content of the carving was kept secret as the faculty of Tamborlain conducted "extensive studies on its meaning and ramifications." Finally, after nearly 15 years of private study, a replica of the carving was released for public viewing.

The carving, it turned out, was a map of Galitia, but not the Galitia of 500 years ago ... Galitia as it stands today. In other words, at the time of the construction of the Third Wall someone created a map showing all five modern walls (as well as most

Tim Bobko

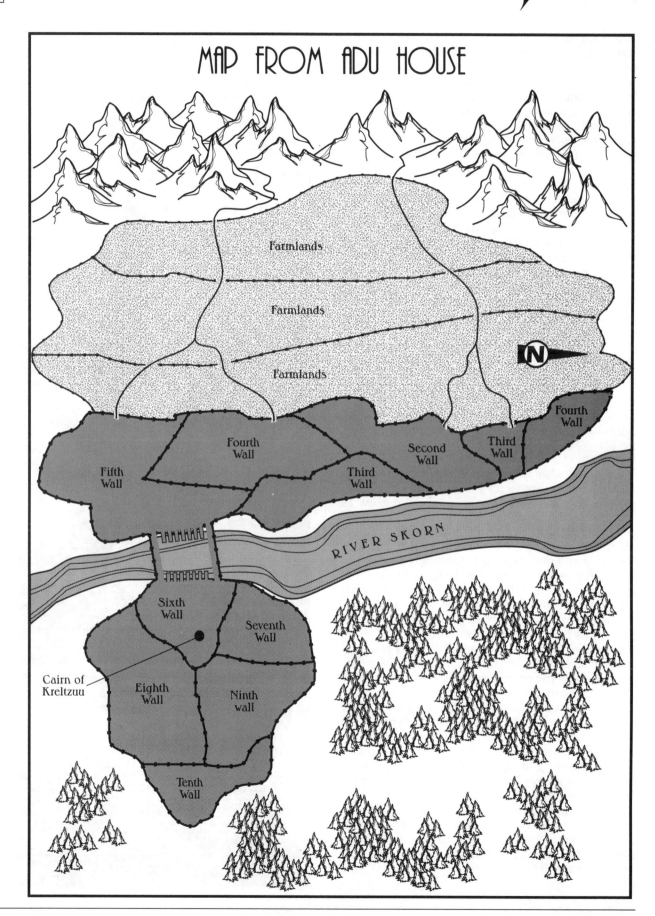

MAP FROM ADU HOUSE

Farmlands

Farmlands

Farmlands

Fifth Wall

Fourth Wall

Third Wall

Second Wall

Third Wall

Fourth Wall

RIVER SKORN

Sixth Wall

Seventh Wall

Cairn of Kreltzuu

Eighth Wall

Ninth wall

Tenth Wall

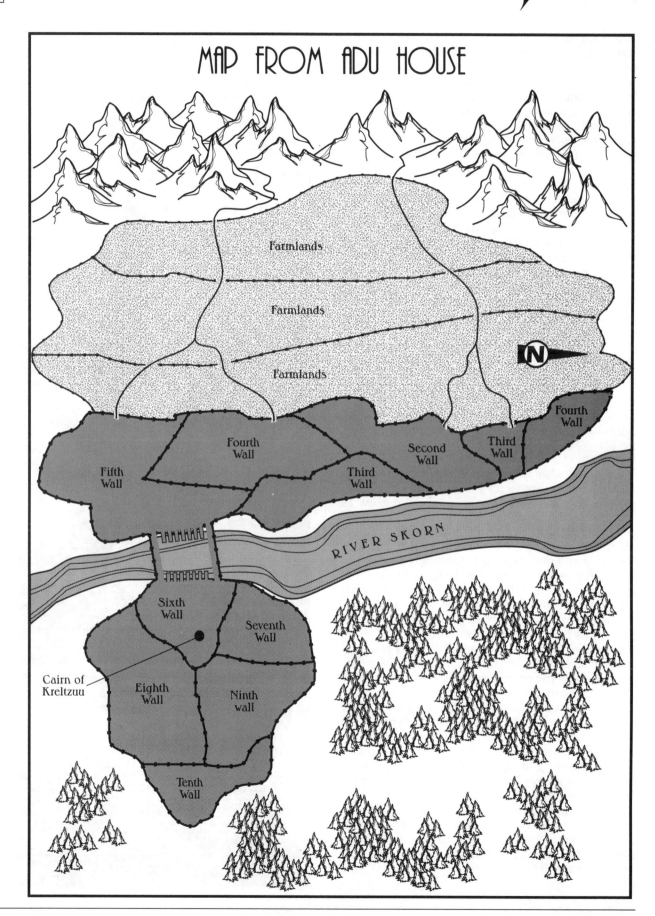

of the major streets and several important buildings) and built it into the foundation of an unspectacular building in an insignificant part of town.

At first the public scoffed at such a claim. Surely the chronomancers were mistaken and the carving was a modern addition to the structure or, at the very most, some power chronomage had aged the carving to make it appear to be vastly older than it was. But the college stood behind the findings of their and the independent mages. The carving was genuine.

The public might have been convinced except for the fact that the college refused to allow public viewing of anything other than the replica (which remains on display at the school's main lecture building to this day). All parties who had seen the original carving were in complete agreement, however, that it should not be made available for general consumption. Adu House was locked and guarded, accessible only with the permission of the Board of Deans of Tamborlain College, and became just another of the hoaxes associated with the poorer parts of the Seers' Quarter.

All that changed a few weeks ago when a reporter for one of the most notorious scandal sheets broke into Adu House, hoping to start a campaign of rumors which would provide material for his daily column. What he found was the best kept secret in a section of town known for "seeing all and telling all."

In the next day's paper, right next to the news report detailing the break-in at Adu House, was his column detailing what could be found inside:

"The stories of a 500-year-old map are only partially true. Yes, there is an map carved into the wood of the ancient building. Yes, it clearly shows the modern structure and details of our fine city. But there is more.

"The depiction of Galitia shows not the three walls of the time when the map was carved, not the five walls of our modern times, but ten walls protecting a city whose borders stretch for kilometers into what is now the most dangerous stretch of Wilderness in the region. This is not an ancient map of Galitia's present, but an amazing glimpse into our future!

"What's more, the walls of the building are covered with writing. Strange, cryptic letters which could spell out anything from the secret of the universe to a delicious recipe for glazed gator-rat."

This report, disreputable though its source was, reignited public interest in Adu House. Crowds formed outside the building every day as everyone from bank managers to blood-cult initiates tried to gain access to the hidden secrets. People were clamoring to know the detailed truth. Did the map show as-yet-unplanned sections of the city in exact-

ADVENURE HOOKS

The mystery of Adu House is left just that … a mystery. Is the map, and the prophetic inscription beside it, genuine? Does it show the future of Galitia and spell the downfall of life as it is known on Marl? What is the ancient race mentioned in the text? When will they return to Galitia? Is there any way other than protecting the ten Great Works to save humanity? All these questions are left to the idividual gamemaster to decide.

✝ The characters have been hired by the Board of Deans to discover the exact location of the Cairn of Kreltzuu. They are to lead an expedition consisting of two professors of magic and five students to the location indicated on the map and to evaluate the site. Travelling even this short distance into the Wilderness is dangerous enough, but when the senior professor is murdered it becomes clear that one member of the party has plans other than study for the cairn. Can the characters fulfill their contract and return alive with the information?

✝ For gamemasters with a more twisted style, the characters are members of a cult which believes that the carvings in Adu House are a message from their patron deity. They must break into the building, decipher the writing and complete the sacred quest the gods have set out for them. Will they perceive the other race to be Demons or the gods themselves? Will they decide to protect the Great Works or level them?

ing detail? What did the writing on the walls say? And could anyone shed any light on how all this came to be in the first place?

The fact is that only a small section of one wall has writing on it, but the language is a very common form of short-hand used by alchemists. The Board of Deans breathed a collective sigh of relief that the reporter was either too scared, too engrossed or too uneducated to notice this fact. Any person in Galitia who has even the most passing interest in chemistry or alchemy would be able to decipher the writing in less than 20 minutes. It says:

"Three Walls to Five Walls to Eight Walls to Ten,
Surround and protect weak, arrogant men.
Galitia, fair city, did shine like a crown
'Til folly and greed brought her tumbling down.
Cut down all the trees, wall off the whole land

Pave over the grass and cement up the sand.
As you sate your great thirst for bigger and more
Give not a thought to who dwelt here before.
For though you banish the Demons and dry out the mud
This land has been steeped with the black, brackish blood
Of a race who sleep longer than our kind may live.
And though protection and courage our mighty walls give
In the face of these creatures they offer us none.
And if we raze the great works that these beings had done
Fear thou their wrath and their terrible ire —
Galitia, doomed city, will perish by fire.
If saving this city is the least of your goals
This building must stand or perish your souls.
And ten other sites must also be saved
You'll know by the mark with which they're engraved
A map of Galitia as she hasn't been seen
And a wisp of a clue from which you can glean
A hint as to where the next site can be found
Some over your heads, others under the ground
But all just as vital to your races survival.
Be sure they're still standing at the great ones' arrival.
To help you get started here's my first little clue,
Within the Seventh Wall is the Cairn of Kreltzuu.
A tree by this tomb is the landmark you seek
And the inscription carved there will clearly speak
Of the next vital spot you must discover and then
Another and another until you've found ten."

Not a classic of Galitian literature, but the message is clear: follow the clue on the map to the Cairn of Kreltzuu and make sure that it is never destroyed.

While one problem arises in that no one has ever heard of Kreltzuu or his cairn, the map in Adu House clearly shows where the site is relative to the rest of the city. The map does indeed show a burgeoning Galitia protected by ten walls rather than the current five. Within the area protected by the fictional, or futuristic, Seventh Wall there is an icon representing a grave with the words "Cairn of K."

This information has not yet been released to the public. All the general populace knows is that the map in Adu House supposedly contains the details of Galitia's future and there is reportedly mystic writings on the walls. The Board of Deans is afraid that the historic building will be vandalized by people seeking to see the carvings for themselves. The Council of Elders is afraid that if this map of a future Galitia is released their as-yet-tentative plans to build a sixth wall will be subject to too much public scrutiny. The seers in the area are all screaming that if the words on the wall are not heeded then every living, and unliving, soul in Galitia will perish.

No one knows for certain whether the map and inscription are genuine or an elaborate fraud, but something will have to be done about them soon. The situation surrounding Adu House gets closer to violence every day. When the details of the carvings are released there is certain to be a race to find the Cairn of Kreltzuu and claim it (and the other eight sites) in the name of one faction or another. Some doomsday factions might even attempt to find the sites for the sole purpose of destroying them, thus "guaranteeing" the eventual extinction of all life in Galitia.

CHAPTER FIVE

PADARR: MAZE OF MURDER

Ever been to Padarr before, mage? You have? Well, have you heard the inside scoop about the Catacombs? Or even that little island in the Bight? Do you know where dreamstones *really* come from? Then how can you say that you *know* the city, nil-head! Got a few hours? I can tell you everything you need to know … for a price. Yeah, that's it. Keep slapping down those osees and it's all yours, mister.

THE SENTRY

You've heard about the evil fortress. You've heard about the mourning sorcerer. But have you heard about the sorcerer's latest plans? Naw, you haven't. And why is that, do you think? Well, you'd probably say that's because nobody in Padarr cares to think about the Sentry. Except me. I know a little about the sorcerer's story. It was passed down through the family to me. The man's name is Gray. He had a daughter once. Now he's mad at the world because he lost her to poor Trista's drunken mother. What do you think the man's been doing on that island for all these centuries. Mourning? Well, he is mourning — in his own way.

Gray had a past before he came to this area. When he got here, he managed to keep his past to himself, especially since the pirates really didn't care to know. You see, there's an unspoken rule in the brotherhood of criminals: Of course, it's more of a protection to the digger than to the guy with the past. Believe me, if you knew certain things about me, well, let's just say you wouldn't be spreading them around unless your spirit was yanked into the middle of a necromancer's ritual party. And even then, I've got connections, bud. Now, if it's your duty to watch someone … but that's an entirely different matter. Gray, needless to say, has quite a past. And his is the kind of past that you've got to watch out for.

First of all, Gray came from a mighty classy family. They lived somewhere even I don't know about. All I, or anyone else, can say about them is that they gave their youngest son the best magical education you could possibly dream about. He probably knows stuff that'll fry your brain if he were to so much as mention it.

But it seems that he didn't want to follow in his parents' footsteps. He had some ideas of his own that he wanted to try. So, one night after a particularly nasty confrontation with his father, Gray went into his laboratory and began working on

Mike Vilardi

something. Now, this something took a long time. Both his father and mother tried to get into the lab, but Gray had taken precautions against such entry. After all, if *you* vomit ferrets when casting a simple *mystic barrier* spell, just think what would happen if Gray were interrupted in the major spell he was performing.

Oh, I didn't tell you which spell he was casting, did I? Well, Gray has on his island a beautiful black crystal which he calls a "Shaping Crystal." It gives people interesting abilities like flight, only you have to take the wings with that one. If you end up being able to breathe fire, then you'll probably resemble something like a fire lizard by the time the crystal's done with you. It's one of those powerful devices that has both positive and negative aspects to it. Although, if you really wanted to look like a fire lizard, then Gray's the man to see.

Where was I? Oh, yeah. Well, Gray was *making* the crystal during those months that he was in the laboratory. Once he was done, he came out and tried to show off his great achievement. But that ain't how it worked out.

The boy came out holding this crystal proudly in front of him. Only, his father and mother weren't so happy. They raged at him until he filled with terrible anger. Without a second thought, he used the crystal on them.

Ever hear tales about Old Missy? Well, that's how his mother ended up. She's a sea snake with the extraordinary talents of underwater breathing and powerful hypnotic suggestion. Get it? Now she has the form of a *water snake*. Ahh! Yeah, now you've got it, ya little ... Ahem. And Gray's father? Well, he kind of became a ghost ... except he's still alive. I'll just tell you his gift. No use wasting any of those gray cells. You have few enough as it is. Gray's father has the power to pass through material objects. Except, now he can't really *do* anything. He just kind of drifts around ... la-de-da. Yep. When Gray made that Shaping Crystal of his, he made it with some minor drawbacks. Of course, if you look at it the right way, you could say that he made a cursed stone that provides a few "advantages" to those it curses. It just depends on how you look at it. Naw. Not really, but I had you going, didn't I? The morphing side effects can be restrained by the wielder of the stone. Notice I said "can be" not "will be." It's up to the wielder of course!

Now you wanna know how to get this fabulous crystal. Do you really think you can handle it? Listen. I'll give you *my* opinion: you can't. Don't even try. Just destroy it. Yeah, that's what I said. Destroy it. There's some other stuff there that'll interest you. Ya gotta think, after all of these years, Gray's got to have some major treasure in there. If he's that stoked up about "performing his magics," well, you know he's gotta have some better stuff than that old crystal.

Why am I concerned? Well, Gray's got something rumbling 'round his head right now: his daughter's death. He doesn't like Padarr. He doesn't like people. He doesn't like much of anything, really. And he doesn't like much of anything enough to get rid of it all. Permanently. That shaping crystal is an integral part of some plan to bring back his daughter. How do I know? Well, ya gotta think. Old Missy did have some relatives, ya little … ahem.

So, you wanna go out there? Well, here's a map of the fortress. Destroy the crystal. Take what you want. Just don't face down old Gray. He's too tough for the likes of you.

For additional material on Gray's background, see page 110 of the *Padarr Citybook*.

THE APPROACH

The approach to the Sentry is tricky. As mentioned on page 27 of *Padarr Citybook*, it can only be approached by one-man skiffs or similar craft because of the silt that has been building up around the island for years. A party could try to walk across the "sandbar" created by the silt, but they'll most likely stumble into quicksilt and "sandworms." Aside from the smaller variety of worm, the island also boasts a few really nasty, large sandworms ready to attack any party that might travel the sandbar. Usually, a party of experienced adventurers warrants one sandworm per character. Of course, if the party has relatively little experience, use one sandworm for every two characters.

As an optional element, the gamemaster could make characters using skiffs roll their *vehicle piloting: boats* or a straight Dexterity at a DN of 10 to see whether the characters can make it to the island without alerting the worms. After all, a slip of the paddle can be just as dangerous as walking.

LARGE SANDWORM
AGILITY 9
Unarmed combat 15
DEXTERITY 7
ENDURANCE 18
Resist shock 19
STRENGTH 15
TOUGHNESS 19
INTELLECT 3
Perception 12, tracking 12
MIND 4
CONFIDENCE 4
Intimidation 10, survival: sandbars 15
CHARISMA 5
Life Points: 5–7 each

Natural Tools: Carapace, armor value TOU +5/24; acid bite, damage value STR +5/20 (the acid causes damage value 25 for five rounds *after* the round the victim was bitten).

Roleplaying Notes: Large sandworms have the ability to notice creatures walking on the sandbar. They "feel" the creature's movements because of the displacement and pressure of the sand in the bar. Once they have determined where the source of the movement is coming from, they will converge on it and come up through the sand to attack. Characters must make a *perception* total of 10 or higher to notice the sandworm's emergence. The sandworms attack by snagging the victim and bringing it down into the water, and then biting until the victim stops moving. Once that happens, the worm burrows into the victim and begins its feast. Since sandworms aren't territorial, they don't attack each other on purpose, nor do they fight over who gets the meal.

THE MAZE

Once the party gets onto the island, they face a complex, ever-changing maze. When Gray originally brought his daughter to the island, he wanted to make her happy. One of the things he did for her amusement was to craft an enchanted maze out of Boteais hedges. The plants move randomly, constantly shifting the pathways that wind through the labyrinth. But always, there is a way through the maze to the fortress, but to find it requires a great deal of time and effort.

The hedge maze completely surrounds the fortress, making the single means of entrance into the keep (except for Gray, who has a password that parts the hedges for him). Since his daughter's death, Gray has added a few interesting (and damaging or deadly) extras to the labyrinth. For example, instead of waiting for someone to pass before moving, Gray has allowed the hedges to hit creatures as they move. Also, he has let loose fearsome monsters to wander the maze, feeding them sparingly to keep their hunger fresh.

Should the party decide to brave the maze, the Boteais hedges immediately begin to writhe and squirm. (See *Hell's Feast* for another example of moving hedges in the world of *Bloodshadows*.) As the characters progress the party might be looking down a long hedge corridor one second only to see it shift into a left turn the next. To simulate this movement, have one of the players roll two ten-sided dice for each group (after all, the party may split up). Check the Maze Chart to see what happens.

Gamemasters should find out the marching order for the party since some of the events in the maze affect characters in a certain position within

CREATING YOUR OWN BOTEAIS MAZE

Boteais hedges are the perfect types of hedges to use for mazes. They grow tall and wide both in the wild and in gardens. Hedges used in mazes must be spelled into shape only once in their lifetimes. From then on they never need to be trimmed or watered. The spell also enhances the hedges' fire resistance ability, increasing their normal Toughness of 27 to 37 versus fire attacks.

One of the other endearing characteristics of these hedges (at least to maze builders) is the thorns that sprout from the inner branches. The thorns can only be seen by the Human eye if they are held up at an angle to the light (much like trying to see a clear plastic splinter). Removing thorns from body parts requires both a *perception* roll against a DN of 9 and a *first aid* roll versus a DN of 10. (It is possible to modify the DN of the *first aid* roll by -1 if someone has tweezers or a needle.) When these thorns pierce and break off in the skin, they provide a distraction factor, effectively lowering the character's Charisma-(because they're bound to be irritable from the stinging pain) and *perception*-related skills.

Luckily, characters expose themselves to these pernicious little thorns only when they try to break through the hedge. Getting smacked by a hedge does not subject the characters to the thorns at all. If a hedge does hit a character, then the damage value is 15, unless stated otherwise.

the group. The avenues of the maze can hold three people across, and each panel of hedges affects the three closest people. So, if a party was marching two people across and three deep, and a hedge panel was to whack them on the left side, the three people on the left side would be affected. If there had been four, then the first three on that side would have been hit, not the last three.

THE FOUNTAIN

Here, at the sight of Gray's daughter's death, stands a large fountain fashioned out of a multi-hued marble. All of the tones in the marble are muted and constantly changing in a whirl of tasteful colors. The statue in the middle consists of several layers of water-spouting fish.

The fountain itself looks like it might have once been cheerful, but without water spraying into the air and without the steady sound of droplets splashing into the collecting pools below, it seems to exude only death. Now only rain water catches in the fountain, stagnant and vile, with a greenish scum floating on the top. The disparity between the beautiful fountain and the wretched water it contains catches even the most blinded of eyes.

Should the characters enter this area, the first thing they notice is a strawberry-blonde girl playing with a strange creature, a beast stolen from someone's nasty nightmare. The large, bipedal creature towers over the girl, its leathery wings flapping slowly and its brilliant red beak chattering in brief spurts. Gray has set up this illusion for those times when he misses his daughter so much that he can hardly bear it. He likes to come to the fountain and just watch her illusion play with the various creatures that he had created for her. With her death, Gray destroyed all of the beasts except for the lassiters. He couldn't stand the horrible memories that Trista's playmates evoked.

If the party watches, they are treated to a scene in which the creature and the daughter play "tea party." Some other exotic and deadly-looking creatures enter from time to time to join in the fun. Trista must have been a joyful child for she seems generous and caring in the illusion.

If a character tries to intervene in the play, he immediately realizes it is an illusion. He also sets off the nasty part of this particular area. There is a Water Imp (*The Unnaturals*, page 33–34) residing in the foul water. Since the illusion takes place around the marble base of the fountain, going near the illusion to try to do something automatically puts that character in range of the Water Imp.

WATER IMP

AGILITY 10
Dodge 15, maneuver 14, unarmed combat 18, unarmed parry 14
DEXTERITY 6
ENDURANCE 10
Resist shock 15
STRENGTH 10
TOUGHNESS 16
INTELLECT 8
Perception 12, trick 15
MIND 8
CONFIDENCE 7
Willpower 12
CHARISMA 6
Life Points: 2–4
Roleplaying Notes: Water Imps have an ad-

MAZE CHART

Die Roll Results

2   You can hear the rustling of hedges but nothing shifts around you. Continue to go forward.

3   There is a left turn ahead. It abruptly becomes a right turn.

4   There is a right turn ahead. As you watch, it becomes a left turn.

5   What was once a straight passage becomes a junction running right and left.

6   What was once a straight passage becomes an elbow junction leading both straight and right.

7   What was once a straight passage becomes an elbow junction leading both straight and left.

8   There is a four-way intersection ahead.

9   What was a dead-end a second ago now leads straight ahead.

10   As you continue forward, a hedge moves sideways, hitting the people on the left. You may go right.

11   You are walking forward when a hedge slams into the right side of the party. You may go left.

12   An ominous rustling can be heard as a hedge moves directly in front of you, hitting the people in the front of the party. You must go back.

13   A hedge rustles behind you and hits the characters at the back of the group. You may go forward.

14   Two hedges move and hit the front and back of the party at the same time. You may go right or left.

15   A hedge moves in such a way that it interposes itself between the party, cutting the groups off from one another.*

16   A hedge moves, exposing the other members of your party that had been separated from you.*

17   There is a movement of the hedges that reveals a fountain.†

18   The hedge in front of you moves to the side and reveals a lassiter readying for the attack. (See *Unnaturals*, pages 73–74)

19   There is a staircase here that leads up to nothing.†

20   A hedges shuffles out of the way, revealing Gray's fortress.

* Gamemasters who don't wish to split the party may use the result listed by 2.

† See the descriptions in the text for further information.

---

vantage versus fire-based spells, gaining an additional +5 to their Toughness. However, each *wound* they take from a fire attack actually causes two *wounds*. For further information, see *The Unnaturals*, page 34. This particular Imp has 100 liters of water to work from, which gives it a Strength of 10 and Toughness of 16.

THE STAIRCASE

The maze has one feature that remains hidden until someone almost stumbles into it. A spiral staircase in the midst of the maze twists upward into the sky, leading to … well, nothing. It looks to be made of steel or some similar metal (not iron) that had at one time been painted white. Now, the paint has peeled off in strips and rust has begun to corrode the railing. Once the party enters the area, the hedges suddenly close behind them. The only remaining exit seems to be up into nowhere.

In reality, this staircase used to lead to an invisible mini-tower where Trista often played. The tower no longer exists, but the staircase remains. If a character attempts to climb the stairs, Nayla, in her Wraith form, attacks.

NAYLA

Species: Wraith
AGILITY 11
Dodge 12, maneuver 13, unarmed combat 17
DEXTERITY 10
ENDURANCE 9
STRENGTH 9
TOUGHNESS 9 (29 w/intangibility)
INTELLECT 7
Trick 10
MIND 7
CONFIDENCE 10

Mike Vilardi

Con 13, intimidation 12
CHARISMA 10
Taunt 14
Life Points: 3
Natural Tools: Intangibility (through Transmutation), armor value TOU+20/29; paralyzing touch, effect value CON+15/25.
Alignment: Chaos 5
Roleplaying Notes: Nayla is quite mad. She killed her daughter, and then was killed herself. Now she will attack anything that gets near her. Her rage is boundless and has turned in on itself so much that she will probably never quite return to her senses — what senses a Wraith has, anyway.

THE FORTRESS

The door that bars entrance to the fortress is made of a strange, purplish wood that comes from a rare tree called the Delantha Everblossom. Despite its name, the Delantha provides a strong wood that can hold spells long past their normal expiration. As a result, Gray only has to bespell his door every other decade or so. The spell he uses on this door allows only recognized faces through — by sight only; it cares not for sound or smell. This door, for example, allows Gray, Trista, and Trista's playmates through. Should a character use her *disguise* skill (DN of 15+ recommended) or some kind of spell (such as *facade*) then she may open the door for the other characters.

THE ENTRY HALL

There isn't much to say about the entry hall except that it is exactly what it sounds like: an entry hall. A grand staircase made of a marble shot through with ebony veins sweeps up to the second level. The hall's floor tiles match the marble of the stairs. Black braziers in each corner shed a strangely brilliant, white glow that casts flickering shadows along the walls, floor, and stairs. Once upon a time, this room might have been the epitome of elegance, but the dull white light from the braziers washes out the color of the once-beautiful tapestries hanging on the walls.

Four slender, black doors at floor level and three up on the balcony remain shut and uninviting.

THE SITTING ROOM

The sitting room's original rich colors and warm wood have faded over time. Evidently, Gray doesn't have much use for this room now, so he's just left it to collect dust. Upon first entrance, light spills in only from the hallway. The characters must devise their own light source to fully illuminate the room. Without sufficient lighting, the characters have a fair chance (*perception* versus a DN of 14) of falling into one of the holes that have rotted through the floorboards (damage value of 10).

THE LIBRARY

Gray still uses the library. Since the ceilings here are rather high (six meters), there are ladders available to help retrieve books from the floor-to-ceiling bookcases. Several well-worn chairs and a few old couches and lounges lay about the room. If the characters spend more than 10 minutes here, they will undoubtedly find at least one book they have some interest in.

Gamemasters, this is where you can have a little fun. Ask the players which book their characters would most like to read. Examples include a book of necromantic spells, a book of love poetry guaranteed to make your lover swoon, a book of knock-knock jokes, etc. Make sure they give fairly specific answers. Now, let them try to find it in this vast library. To find their book, they will have to beat a DN of 20 with a *perception* or *deduction* roll. If someone managed to find their book, then let her have it. If not, allow the people who missed to try again. For game purposes, every attempt equals ten minutes of searching. Eventually, characters either find their book, waste a lot of time looking, or both.

Upon reading the book, the character receives a skill add in a skill relevant to the subject of the tome. For example, a character who sought out a book of conjuring spells finds an excellent treatise on the art of conjuring. After reading it for 2–20 hours (roll two ten-sided dice), she gains an add in the skill of *conjuration*. The same holds true for someone who found a book of love poetry. That person gains a skill add in *charm*.

THE STUDY

The wood-paneled study has a large desk and a large, round wooden table surrounded by eight chairs. A large map on the table charts out the continent of Caldov. If the characters look closely, they see several red squiggles drawn onto the map around the area of an unidentified major city. A few similar red marks appear around Jeboa, a city on this continent just opposite the unnamed metropolis on Caldov.

On the desk, several dreamstones sit in a lopsided pile. The stones contain various dreams of Trista's that Gray had captured for her. He continually transfers them to other stones when the current dreamstones start fading away.

THE INNER GREENHOUSE AND AVIARY

Unlike the rest of the fortress, this section seethes with life — dozens of different species of plants and

Mike Vilardi

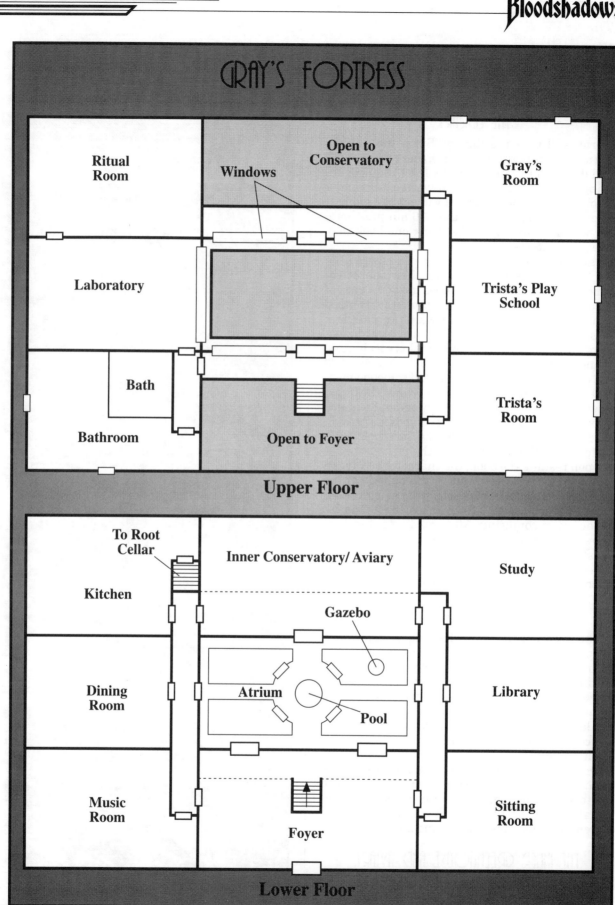

GRAY'S FORTRESS

Ritual Room

Open to Conservatory

Windows

Gray's Room

Laboratory

Trista's Play School

Bath

Bathroom

Open to Foyer

Trista's Room

Upper Floor

To Root Cellar

Inner Conservatory/ Aviary

Study

Kitchen

Gazebo

Atrium

Pool

Dining Room

Library

Music Room

Foyer

Sitting Room

Lower Floor

birds crowding each other out for space. The warm, humid air steams up the glass of the walls and the ceiling high above. Sunlight filters into the room during the day, hitting dust motes or causing the fine spray that occasionally mists the plants to sparkle and shimmer with rainbows.

The greenhouse is definitely in excellent working order. The plants are healthy and the birds are constantly calling out or diving across the room in a colorful swoosh of feathers. Gray uses this room to divert his attention from whatever he is researching at the time. A small section of herbs, grains, vegetables, and fruits supplies Gray with a constant source of food.

THE ATRIUM

A number of window and a balcony running around the upper level look out onto this, the middle courtyard of the fortress. The overhang of the balcony allows for some protection from the elements on those days when it snows or rains. A small stone footpath runs from door to door directly under the balcony.

A spell cast during the building of the pool that stands at the center of the courtyard keeps the water clear and potable. Once again, the pool is crafted from of marble, but it has a soft green glow to it that lights up the atrium at night. Several benches carved from the same glowing marble surround the pool.

The paint on the small, wooden gazebo in the northeast corner of the atrium has begun to peel, though the wood beneath still looks sound.

Anyone walking along the paths feels as if an inhuman presence has taken up stride with him. But efforts to locate that presence fail, for the spirit that haunts this place remains intangible to the mundane senses. If a character attempts to contact the spirit — the remaining energy of a long-dead servant named Julius Merkong — and succeeds at a Charisma check versus a DN of 18, the spirit materializes into a dark silhouette capable of communicating telepathically with the character. Julius can tell of Gray's tale, but he knows nothing about what has happened since Trista and Nayla perished. Before he shifts back into his intangible form, he tells the characters to leave as soon as they can. There's no telling what Gray will do in his current state.

THE MUSIC ROOM

The music room is filled with various instruments of the finest quality. A piano and a harpsichord sit facing each other on opposite sides of the room. Next to the piano stands an elegant harp carved from the same purplish wood as that of the main door to the fortress. There is a flute resting on the harpsichord, and a violin hanging on a music stand right next to it. On the other side of the piano, a cello rests against the wall. Scattered throughout the room are various chairs and a loveseat. If the characters beat a DN of 6 with *perception*, they notice that all of the stringed instruments were designed for a child.

Gray had wished for his daughter to learn how to play music. He wanted his daughter to be as well-rounded as he was. After all, some of the skills that he learned in magic were a lot easier to grasp by using music. Gray even has a few spells that require him only to hum a tune or sing a note to trigger them.

If the characters pick up an instrument, it enlarges to fit their size. This was another of Gray's gifts to his daughter. Since he believed that she would wish to use the instruments for most of her life, he had managed to create spells that would allow for an adjustment in size. The characters can try to leave with some of the instruments, but the piano, harpsichord, and harp require a Strength roll versus a DN of 25 to remove, for some side effect of the spells Gray devised created a strong magical bond between the room and the instruments. Of course, the characters will have to take an *artist* skill to be able to play any of the instruments with some semblance of musicality.

As a point of interest, there are several pieces of sheet music lying around. Some are classical, some jazzy, some hand-written compositions. There is also a staff notebook with some notes written in a childish scrawl.

THE DINING ROOM

A long, wooden table that seats about 20 dominates the dining room. At the head and foot of the table are two chairs that are different from the rest. One is almost a throne, the other a miniature booster version of the larger one. A thin layer of gray dust covers the entire room. The tapestries hanging from the walls have become faded and dust-ridden. The faint smell of mildew accompanies each breath inhaled by someone in the room.

THE KITCHEN

The kitchen contains a large fireplace with a small bread-baking oven off to one side. There are also several tables and two large sinks that have running water. Grease stains mar the tiled floor and a half-dozen pieces of black, rotted fruit sit in a clump atop the table. A dark staircase leads down to a root cellar (which the gamemaster is encouraged to create and detail).

TRISTA'S ROOM

This room has a cream-colored decor set against its gold-trimmed wooden panels. A fluffy bed with a set of steps leading up to it rests in the exact center. Stuffed animals, several "handled" dolls, a beautiful music box with a dancer, and other assorted items that would be owned by a pampered young girl lie scattered about the bed and floor. The wardrobe contains frilly and plain dresses, pajamas, cute little shoes, and other articles of clothing appropriate for a well-off little girl. In fact, characters who abhor sentimentality almost become nauseated at the sight of so much "cuteness." One thing to note about this room is that it is as "neat as a pin." Gray has kept it so as a memorial to his daughter.

TRISTA'S PLAYROOM AND SCHOOLROOM

The three varnished wooden tables lining the walls of the room each have two matching chairs. On the fourth wall, in which the door is set, hang two chalkboards and several maps. The maps faded long ago, but some markings can still be made out. A successful *perception* roll against a DN of 15 allows a character to read a few of the words (alter the number of readable words depending on the success level of the *perception* roll): Caldo…, gateway, link, old ones, war.

In one of the corners sits a box filled with toys and puzzles. Each one of the toys has some educational purpose, but they also look like fun. Any character who touches a toy or puzzle feels the irresistible urge to play with it (to put down the amusement requires a *willpower* roll versus a DN of 14). Unbeknownst to Gray, the toys have absorbed some of the strange magical energies coming from his laboratory, thereby creating this strange effect.

GRAY'S ROOM

Gray's bedroom is rather austere and masculine. The bed has dark linens, the wardrobe is full of plain and colorful robes, and old-fashioned and modern suits. Though the clothes seem worn and faded, they bear a certain regal quality, definitely not the wardrobe of commoners.

On the bedstands, one on either side of the bed, is a collection currency ranging from selasts to Caldovian notes — all crisp or clean and stacked in two neat piles. Evidently, Gray still gets around.

THE BATHROOM

This is one of the most ornate bathrooms that money can buy. The toilet/sink/bath combination is crafted of gilded steel, and the deep, ceramic bath-pool spans almost two-and-a-half meters. A girl of eight could definitely have a lot of fun with bubbles in that sunken tub. Warm water constantly flows from a pair of gleaming silver faucets, so it must either be supplied by a hot spring, bespelled by an intricate enchantment, or both. Having such a setup on the second floor is quite amazing in itself, but then, that's where expensive contractors come in.

THE LABORATORY

Gray spends most of his time here. He continually researches, hypothesizes, experiments, and tweaks various projects. Several long tables bear all manner of glassware, components, and other materials. Depending on what Gray is working on, there could be beakers, test tubes, boiling liquids, crushed herbs in a mortar, or other such paraphernalia present.

Depending on how you wish to present Gray to the characters, you could describe the whole room innocently, or you could add ominous overtones. For example, Gray may have left something boiling for a while. Describe the boiling pot as "spitting putrid green fumes out into the impersonal lab." This slant allows the gamemaster to hint at Gray's evil nature.

THE RITUAL ROOM

The ritual room is not only used for ritual, but also for scrying and communications. It consists of black walls and ceiling with a permanent pentagram drawn on the floor in gold paint. To be sure of its continued potency, Gray redraws the design every year.

A small black table in one corner holds a scrying bowl, a ritual dagger, and a few candles of various colors. The most important thing in the room, however, is a collection of seven different crystals. Check the Crystal Chart below to find the appropriate property.

If the gamemaster wishes, it is possible to forward the plot by placing Trista's ghost in this room. Ever since her death, she has been watching her father's work. If Gray is evil, she tries to help the characters. If Gray is good, she tries to inform the characters of that fact.

TRISTA

Species: Ghost
AGILITY 9
Stealth 13
DEXTERITY 9
ENDURANCE 8
STRENGTH 8
TOUGHNESS 9 (29 w/intangibility)
INTELLECT 12

CRYSTAL CHART

Color	Property
Fiery Red	Can be the shaping crystal if the black stone holds Gray's mental attributes, otherwise, gamemaster's choice of spells and charges.
Clear	Automatically casts *light* when "Light, please" is spoken. 15 charges.
Deep Purple	Automatically casts *detect magic* when "Is it magic?" is said. 22 charges.
Black	Receptacle for Gray's mental attributes or the shaping crystal.
Light Blue	Automatically casts *first aid* when "Heal and be well!" is spoken. 9 charges.
Emerald Green	Automatically casts *communicate with animal* when "speak" is spoken. 10 charges.
Sea Green	Automatically casts *facade* when "Change me" is spoken. 18 charges.

Cantrips 14, divination: vitomancy 13, divination: wizardry 14, first aid 13, perception 15
MIND 11
Conjuration: photomancy 13
CONFIDENCE 10
Alteration: vitomancy 13, willpower 14
CHARISMA 10
Charm 11
Life Points: 1
Spells: *Awaken, communicate with animal, detect magic, first aid, intuition, light*
Cantrips: *Chill, clean, find, heat, note*
Arcane Knowledges: Earth, folk, light, living forces, magic
Natural Tools: Cold touch, damage value Endurance +3/11; intangibility, armor value TOU+20/29; invisibility (*stealth* +10)
Alignment: Oathbreaker Order 10
Roleplaying Notes: Trista was once a sweet child of eight. When her mother killed her, she felt the need to stay around and watch over her father. Gray had taken her loss badly — in fact, he continues to do so. For good or for bad, Trista is just trying to help her father in any way possible. One thing that she won't do, however, is show herself in to him. She would not want to open his wounds of grief any wider.

HOW TO USE GRAY'S FORTRESS

Gray's fortress is an excellent place to set an adventure. In fact, a gamemaster could use the set up at the beginning of this chapter to start off an adventure. A party of individuals are approached by a hooded stranger. They get to talking about Padarren lore. The subject of the Sentry comes up. The next thing you know, the stranger is enticing the characters out to the fortress by telling them about a treasure. If you follow the story closely it is possible to come up with several motivations for

the stranger. The following adventure hooks provide you with just a few of the possibilities.

THE STRAIGHT DOPE

The stranger is telling the complete truth. He's a relative of Gray and was sent to Padarr to keep an eye on his unhinged relative. Recently he has become concerned that Gray is up to something evil. He can have an altruistic motive to stop Gray, such as wishing to prevent the destruction that he suspects Gray is planning. Or, he can have a purely personal reason. For example, the stranger doesn't want Gray to do something else that will embarrass the family back where he comes from, or perhaps the stranger has some monetary concerns that he doesn't want Gray to foil. If this is how you wish to run Gray, make sure to add a few more nasty Unnaturals to Gray's maze, and set up a few choice encounters in the fortress. For an additional twist, have the characters meet Gray. He could seem perfectly sane and genuinely sad over his daughter's death all those years ago. Make the characters sympathize with him — even believe him. If you wish, you could even have Gray start portraying the stranger as the evil one, sent by the elders of his family to destroy him. Then, when the characters least expect it … WHAM! Gray does something utterly horrible to the party at worst possible time!

WITH A TWIST OF DECEPTION

The stranger is a relative of Gray, but harbors great resentment toward him. He wants the characters to destroy the black crystal, and will offer whatever sum the characters request for the job. The stranger wants what the crystal contains: Gray's mental Attributes.

Gray uses the stone to hold his conscious mind while he journeys around Marl in an astral form.

This is more of a protection from other astral bodies than anything else. Gray, of course, believes that his fortress is safe from entry. Once the characters reach the ritual room where the crystals sit unprotected, they also find Gray on the floor, apparently dead. Of course, he is just in his astral form. Before the characters decide to destroy the black crystal, which will effectively destroy Gray, have the ghost of Trista show up and try to persuade them otherwise. Whether the characters go ahead and destroy the black crystal or not, they will have to find out about the stranger and try to stop him. The stranger could then arrive and turn out to be the characters' arch-nemesis.

ALL THINGS BEING THE SAME

Perhaps both the stranger and Gray have evil natures. Gray wants to destroy Padarr, or something equally as nasty. The stranger wishes to destroy Gray so that he can follow through on his own plans without the constant interference that Gray has been giving him. Once the characters destroy Gray, they find out from Trista's ghost that the stranger can now perform his chaotic plans. This version of events could span several adventures.

OTHER POSSIBILITIES

It is possible to plant a few other interesting treasures on Sentry Island. Here are just a few ideas.

 Old Missy is tearing up the sea lanes to the north. In fact, it's gotten so bad that merchants refuse to ship things that way anymore. A rumor surfaces that the sorceror on the island could help somehow, and the Padarren government decides to secretly hire a group to contact the mage. The characters have to persuade Gray to change his mother back into a Human. It can be done — with the correct ritual. If Gray agrees, he needs the eye of a whaler to perform the casting.

† A plague threatens Padarr. Already many have fallen to the contagion. One of the professors at the Arcanum has had a dream that leads him to believe that the Sentry somehow holds the cure. If the party is willing, they may visit the island and try to persuade Gray to help. Of course, there is a reward being offered from the city and the Arcanum.

GRAY

Gray originally comes from a city that he wants to forget about. His parents were both dimensional sorcerers and wanted him to be the same, but he rebelled. After causing both of his parents to be changed seemingly irreversibly into *other* things, Gray left and came to the site where Padarr exists today. Over the years, he has gathered knowledge of just about everything magical. He is an excellent researcher and theorist in the field of magic, though he is reticent to trade that information for money — which does not rule out an exchange of magic.

GRAY

Species: Human
AGILITY 9
Dodge 11, melee combat 10, running 10, stealth 10
DEXTERITY 9
Fire combat 10, thrown weapons 12
ENDURANCE 8
STRENGTH 8
TOUGHNESS 9
INTELLECT 13
Apportation: (choose three) 16, cantrips 17, divination: (choose three) 16, first aid 14, linguistics 14, perception 16, science: chemistry 14, teaching 14, trick 14
MIND 13
Artist: music 15, cartography 14, conjuration: (choose three) 16, medicine 14, research 17, scholar: magic 16
CONFIDENCE 11
Alteration: (choose three) 14, willpower 15
CHARISMA 8
Persuasion 11, summoning: (choose three) 13
Life Points: 7
Spells: See roleplaying notes.
Cantrips: *Breeze, chill, clean, find, heat, note*
Arcane Knowledges: See roleplaying notes.
Alignment: See roleplaying notes.
Roleplaying Notes: Gray has lived for hundreds of years. He has prolonged his life through various spells and rituals. Because of his age, he has known (and forgotten) most spells at one time or another. As a result, Gray knows all of the spells in *The World of Bloodshadows* as well as many others not revealed in that tome. As a gamemaster, it is

Tim Bobko

up to you to choose which spells, foci, and arcane knowledges Gray might possess based on how you wish to use him in a campaign. For example, if Gray is peaceful, then he would probably have more defensive spells in his current repertoire. If you wish to play him as evil, then put more offensive spells in his grimoire. Gray was purposefully left open for the gamemaster to use as he or she wishes. The gamemaster can therefore apply him in a way that supports and furthers the feel of the campaign.

THE POWERS THAT BE

Padarr is run by a bureaucracy, which governs almost every aspect of city life. These bureaucrats can be formidable opponents for the player characters — but they can also be the launching points for adventure. They have the resources to know when and where things happen; a vested interest in sparking events or quashing them; and the money to pay for the best to carry out their wills.

The *Padarr Citybook* presents a great deal of information about the way the city works, but a little more never hurts. Characters operating out of this town are most likely to get contracted by the Management Committee or one of the divisions it oversees, so here are some more details on that.

THE MANAGEMENT COMMITTEE

The bureaucracy is ultimately controlled by the so-called "Management Committee." There are nine seats on the Committee, and its memebers — theoretically, at least — control all aspects of life within the bureaucracy. All decisions made by the Committee are by open ballot. Resolutions — which can be proposed by any member — are carried on a simple majority of votes.

Within the Management Committee, it's considered a personal shame to propose a resolution that's subsequently voted down — particularly if the margin of votes against it is very wide. Because of this, Committee members are very tentative about proposing anything that might change the status quo. When a member puts forward any resolution whatsoever, she'll go to great lengths "lobbying" other members to her point of view before putting the resolution on the table. Of course, this leads to an epic amount of horse-trading and influence-peddling when a major resolution is forthcoming.

The Committee often polarizes around two or three highly influential, aggressive and ruthless members, with the others forming loose coalitions or alliances to support whoever they think will benefit them the most in the long run.

FILLING SEATS

People named to the Committee retain their seats for life, until they retire, or until their rivals aropund the big boardroom manage to oust them in disgrace. When a seat on the Committee is vacated, the remaining Committee members are free to propose replacements — but only from the rarefied ranks of upper bureaucracy management, of course — and then the Committee members vote on the candidates. To be accepted onto the Committee, a candidate must receive votes from at least three-quarters of the sitting members; in the case where a single seat must be filled, this means the victorious candidate needs six votes.

According to the Management Committee's formal charter, no business can be conducted until any and all vacant seats are filled. This is the only reason that wrangles over new Committee members don't turn into eternal deadlocks. Eventually, enough people have to agree on *some* compromise candidate, in order to get back to real work again.

Predictably there's much political maneuvering, posturing and infighting around the nomination and election of new members to the Committee.

PRIVILEGES AND PERKS

Unlike the City Fathers, the members of the Management Committee don't automatically receive perquisites like cars and drivers, tax-free stipends, robes of office or shapely silver golems. The fiction is that the Committee members are truly loyal "servants of the people," and so shouldn't enjoy any such trappings.

What they do enjoy, however, are huge salaries: 400,000 osees per year, plus bonuses for additional duties (and whatever squeeze they can glom onto, of course). This salary is taxable, but that still means their take-home pay is 300,000 osees per

annum — more than twice what the City Fathers receive. While they don't get free use of a luxury car, they can easily afford to buy themselves several, and hire all the drivers and bodyguards they'd ever need.

COMMITTEE MEMBERS

Unlike the City Fathers, the members of the Management Committee keep a low public profile. Few people on the streets of Padarr could name even one, let alone all nine, of the Committee members ... despite the fact that these individuals arguably have more effect over day-to-day life than the City Fathers.

What you need to remember is that, just because the characters aren't aware of the Committee members, doesn't mean the Committee members aren't aware of *them*. Meetings will probably be held in out of the way places, with the Committee members possibly even trying to keep their identities hidden. It's doubtful they'll want to be publicly associated with the characters, and the characters might want to think twice about exposing them ... at least, if they want to stay alive and well and living in Padarr.

MAJOR DIVISIONS

The overall bureaucracy is divided into scores of departments and "offices," each semi-autonomous within the greater administration. People outside the administration find it difficult, if not impossible, to keep track of the different divisions. They seem to shift and alter, changing name, location, personnel and responsibility with no warning. One year, Proctors' salaries are handled by the Payroll Department, for example, while the next the Internal Finance Office has jurisdiction. Then suddenly it's the Fiscal Disbursement Service, and nobody in the bureaucracy will admit there even *was* an Internal Finance Office once ...

A couple of major departments seems permanent. (Note that this list is *far* from exhaustive ...)

† **Civic Planning Office:** Currently managed by Denny Jurt, this is the department responsible for issuing — or, more commonly — *rejecting* — building applications and requests for rezoning.

† **Personnel:** Arguably the largest "empire" within the bureaucracy, this is responsible for hiring and firing (only very rarely the latter). The Recruitment Sub-Office seems to be doing a hell of a job: the civil service grew over three percent last year alone. The Director of Personnel is one Alathea Blyss (who is maneuvering for a seat on the Management Committee).

† **Inland Revenue Office:** The dreaded IRO is responsible for tax collection in al its multiplicity of forms. It liaises closely with the Customs and Excise Branch ... or at least it *should*. In fact, a turf war between the two departments has been raging for the past couple of years. The new IRO Director — Laiza Smed — has a reputation as a lethal political infighter, which bodes ill for an interdepartmental cooperation in the foreseeable future.

† **Customs and Excise Branch:** This department administers customs, tariffs and duties on incoming shipments, whether the cargo is intended for sale in Padarr or whether it's just passing through. The Branch Manager is Jan Hart — an ex-mercenary, if popular rumors are to be believed — and a creditable opponent for the IRO's Smed.

CHAPTER SIX

GWALIOR: CITY IN RUIN

The city of Gwalior has had more than its share of trouble as of late. With horrors swarming up from the sewers, and the zealots of the Red Hand raising Terrors from the darkness, the city is barely fit for Sk'rats, let alone Humans. The empty-headed lore peddlers of the area warn of dire events to come, for these "trivial" occurrences — as they call them — mark only the beginning of the end. Though most citizens ignore such drivel, some do believe in the prophecies that were born out of the first Godwar. To save themselves, their families, and the rest of Gwalior, they have begun to take action to defend themselves against the approaching threat.

Stone markers carved with runes dating back to the first Godwar tell a story which may have more than a little to do with the recent strife in the area. According to translations, the stretch of land where Gwalior now stands was the site of a major battle between the forces of Order and Chaos. The Chaos armies were led by a being called Zagwannorr, Brood Mistress of Corruption. Most tales of Zagwannorr tell of her wicked powers, with each legend adding a different ability to her arsenal. The only thread of consistency involves her power to change creatures into chaotic monstrosities, which most tales show her doing with only a touch.

The carvings also indicate that the final battle against Zagwannorr, in which she fell beneath the forces of Order, occurred here in the lands surrounding Gwalior. Unfortunately, Darlock of Order had not the might to end her existence; he could only seal away her within a great casket of lead. Powerful wards would prevent her escape by keeping the Chaos Lord in a state of perpetual slumber. Her great army was decimated and driven from the field by Darlock's forces, who then carried the great coffin to the ocean, where they hid it beneath the waves, hopefully for all eternity. Darlock and his army followed the casket down to the murky sea floor where they stand as undying guardians against Zagwannorr's return.

To this day, Zagwannorr lives trapped in enchanted slumber, her dreams filled with bloodlust and conquest. As the dawning of a new Godwar approaches, she twists and turns more restlessly. The spells that bind her have weakened through the long age of her imprisonment, allowing her aura of corruption to seep out and twist the wildlife near Gwalior, creating horrors like gator-rats, blood urchins, grime sharks, bloated Undead, and other hideous creatures. These horrors and the men that worship Chaos can feel her dreams, and they have begun to work toward freeing their mistress so that she can lead them into battle once more and anoint herself with the blood of the living.

ADVENTURE SYNOPSIS

This adventure works best with relatively experienced *Bloodshadows* characters. If characters fail the task set before them in this adventure, death is the least of their worries, as the entire region near Gwalior could be destroyed if the Chaos Lord Zagwannorr is freed.

The adventure is set in the area around the city of Gwalior. Gamemasters unfamiliar with the region can find full information on the city in the *Wilderness* sourcebook.

In the first scene of the adventure, the characters find out about a strange "sleeping sickness" affecting people in the area. When normal magical medicinals prove ineffective in preventing the spread of the disease, a somniomancer is called in to fight the plague. The characters are hired to escort the mage to Gwalior from whichever city they are currently in. Though the route places the characters and their charge in danger, it is no different from any other trek through the Wilderness.

In the second scene, the somniomancer discovers the source of the contagion, and the characters are called upon to travel once more into the Wilderness to find an enchanted tablet which will provide clues to who or what is behind the strange plague. Chaos-tainted warriors seek to block the characters at every turn.

The third scene opens with the victims of the sleeping sickness rising under the control of Zagwannorr, and marching into the sea. Each drowning death strengthens the Chaos Lord and weakens the enchanted bonds that hold her. The characters must travel to the her tomb and reactivate the wards that bind her to prevent her return to Marl. The tomb-prison rests 100 meters under water in a cave filled with Chaos-twisted servants eager for the release of their dark mistress.

Since this scenario can begin in any city the characters happen to be in, you have several options for bringing them into the adventure. Wilderness guides, mercenaries, or bodyguards could see or hear of an advertisement for the job. Anyone who just needs money might also take interest in the assignment, and show up at the address listed on the notice. Some characters may even have family members in Gwalior. If they hear that the city requires a somniomancer to quell a spreading plague, they might offer their services in an effort to bring relief before their own family members fall to the disease.

SCENE ONE: TO CHALLENGE THE UNKNOWN

THE SITUATION

Standard. This scene occurs at a small mage's shop, the address of which appeared on the advertisement requesting escort. Tandway, a well-known and well-respected local somniomancer, needs a group to accompany him through the Wilderness to Gwalior. There's been an outbreak of some sort of sleeping disease and the people of Gwalior are in great need of a magician that specializes in sleep and sleep magic.

TANDWAY

AGILITY 9
Climbing 10, dodge 12, stealth 11
DEXTERITY 8
Fire combat 11, thrown weapons 10
ENDURANCE 7
STRENGTH 6
TOUGHNESS 8 (10 w/armor)
INTELLECT 12
Apportation: somniomancy 16, cantrips 20, divination: somniomancy 15, first aid 13, perception 14
MIND 11
Conjuration: somniomancy 14, hypnotism 15
CONFIDENCE 10
Alteration: somniomancy 18, willpower 15
CHARISMA 9
Persuasion 13, summoning: somniomancy 13
Life Points: 7
Alignment: Order 2
Equipment: .38 Gelvash revolver; glowstone flashlight; leather coat (armor value TOU+2/17); Hand of Glory (three charges); two potions of *thunder*; various magical accoutrements.
Spells: *Awaken, healing sleep (as first aid spell), sleep of the dead*
Note: Most of Tandway's spells will prove to be useless on a long overland adventure. Somniomancy spells deal primarily with sleep and dreaming. He will use any spells that seem appropriate to help deal with threats, but this is why he's hired the characters.
Cantrips: *Breeze, chill, clean, find, heat, note*
Arcane Knowledges: Death 2, Life 2, Living Forces 3, Folk 2, Magic 1, Enchanted 1
Description: Tandway is a quiet, driven man. He is unusual for a mage in that he isn't aloof, puts on no false pretenses, and is willing to get his hands dirty along side the "hirelings" to ensure the success of his mission. Tandway is meticulous and

Jaime Lombardo & Ron Hill

efficient, and seems to have a gift for putting people where they'll do the most good (or the least harm.) Tandway is young for a magician of his power and position, being in his late thirties. He has sharp features, giving him a "hawkish" appearance, and dresses in common work clothes rather than the foppish robes that many of his ilk wear. The only thing that betrays his true calling is the ruby apparently set into his forehead, which flickers with a crimson light when he casts spells or is engaged in deep thought.

THE ACTION

The characters arrive to find Tandway already packing up spell components for the trip. He seems preoccupied as he explains the situation to the characters. He tells them that he must leave immediately and can offer each member of the group 100 Galitian vens per day, plus reasonable outfitting expenses.

Since he is desperate, however, he can be bargained up to 125 vens per day, plus a free spell once the group reaches Gwalior. Tandway must leave no later than tomorrow morning, and will do all he can to speed the preparations along.

The trip to Gwalior is fraught with peril. It will take a number of days or weeks to get there, depending on where your *Bloodshadows* campaign is set. Some suggested encounters have been pro-

vided below to ensure an exciting trip (roll 1d10 to select an encounter). Use some or all the encounters as you see fit, or generate your own encounters using the *Wilderness* sourcebook.

ENCOUNTERS IN THE WILDERNESS

1. Granite Cats (Mountains and Hills)
2. Rocks (Mountains and Hills)
3. Sand Skeletons (Desert)
4. Sand Sharks (Desert)
5. Nitrars (Swamp)
6. Giant Slugs (Swamp)
7. Queskworms (Any)
8. Duraz (Any)
9. Gamemaster's Choice
10. Gamemaster's Choice

GRANITE CATS

This encounter works best at night. The party becomes the prey of a hunting pack of granite cats, one foe for each party member and mount. The cats approach silently; the party only receives warning if some sort of warding or alarm spell is active or if one of the camp guards generates a *perception* total of 20 or more. The granite cats attack until either

all their prey is dead or more than half of their own have been killed.

GRANITE CAT

AGILITY 13
Acrobatics 16, climbing 17, long jumping 15, maneuver 15, running 15, stealth 16 (19 if stationary near a rock wall), unarmed combat 15, unarmed parry 15
DEXTERITY 11
ENDURANCE 13
Resist shock 15
STRENGTH 14
TOUGHNESS 13
INTELLECT 4
Perception: smell 14
MIND 3
CONFIDENCE 9
Intimidation 13
CHARISMA 7
Life Points: 1-2
Natural Tools: Claws, damage value STR+3/17, teeth damage value STR+1/15
Roleplaying Notes: Granite cats are so named because they blend into gray walls, making them almost invisible. They resemble nothing more than 13–20' long lions made of a dense, stone material.

ROCKS

This encounter works any time of day. As the party travels through a high mountain pass, the sun suddenly winks out. The gigantic shape of a bird is winging by overhead, blotting out the sunlight. Just as suddenly, the monstrous bird releases a boulder from its talons, trying to crush the group. The rock continues to harass the party until they leave the mountains or until it manages to crush something for dinner.

ROCK

AGILITY 12
Flight 13, maneuver 13, stealth 14 (gliding 16), unarmed combat 13
DEXTERITY 14
Missile weapons 14 (boulder dropping 18)
ENDURANCE 16
STRENGTH 22
TOUGHNESS 18
INTELLECT 2
Perception 11
MIND 2
CONFIDENCE 13
Intimidation 16
CHARISMA 6
Life Points: 1
Natural Tools: Talons, damage value STR+6/28, beak, damage value STR+4/26. Boulders have

a mass of 400 kilograms(value 13), and are usually dropped from a height of about 250 meters (value 12). Anyone hit by one takes a damage value of 25 plus bonus (minimum of +1). A standard size boulder is large enough to hit two people standing side-by-side.

Roleplaying Notes: Rocks are gigantic, hawk-like birds with wingspans of up to 20 meters. They have earned their unusual name from their unique hunting method. Rocks enjoy their food pulped to almost liquid, and as a result they hunt by dropping huge boulders down on unsuspecting prey. Rocks are masters of stealth and are rarely spotted until it's too late.

SAND SKELETONS

This encounter works well during the daytime, especially when the group is searching for a good place to camp. A set of small dunes surround an oasis. When the characters walk on the dunes, the sand explodes violently outward, and several gigantic skeletons suddenly appear (one for every two party members). The sand skeletons ignore pack and riding animals, concentrating instead on intelligent creatures. During the first round of attack the characters should be completely surprised, giving the sand skeletons a +3 on all attacks and damage rolls that round.

SAND SKELETON

AGILITY 9
Maneuver 11, melee combat 13 (club 15), stealth 11
DEXTERITY 6
ENDURANCE 16
STRENGTH 18
TOUGHNESS 20
INTELLECT 2
Camouflage 14, perception 14
MIND 2
CONFIDENCE 13
Intimidation 14
CHARISMA 2
Life Points: 2
Equipment: Bone club, damage value STR+4/22
Roleplaying Notes: Sand skeletons are giant undead skeletons that hide beneath desert dunes. No one knows who or what created them, or why they have been instructed to do what they do, but they continue to be a major hazard to those who dare to travel through the deserts of Marl.

SAND SHARKS

This encounter is especially dangerous and nasty if sprung on the party during the night. At least five, but up to 10 sand sharks lie in wait in the area

Jaime Lombardo & Ron Hill

the party has decided to camp. At some point after midnight, the sharks attack any characters standing guard, as well as one or two sleeping characters. The creatures swim through sand like normal sharks move through water. They attack by coming up under a target and biting its legs, and then carry the prey under the sands where it can be eaten leisurely.

SAND SHARKS

AGILITY 13
Maneuver 14, stealth 14, swimming 15, unarmed combat 14
DEXTERITY 5
ENDURANCE 12
STRENGTH 12
TOUGHNESS 12 (14 w/armor)
INTELLECT 2
Trick 5
MIND 2
CONFIDENCE 10
Intimidation 13
CHARISMA 3
Life Points: 1
Natural Tools: Teeth, damage value STR+4/16; leathery hide, armor value TOU+2/14
Roleplaying Notes: These creatures bear features almost identical to normal sharks, except for the fact that they move through and breath in sand

and loose soil rather than water. The sand shark has no sense of sight, instead it "sees" through a process similar to radar. It can detect the slightest motion or disturbance within 100 meters. Sand sharks have light tan to dusky brown skin, which helps them blend with their surroundings.

NITRAR

Nitrars make a good encounter for a party traveling through or near a swamp. If the group has had a rough time on the overland thus far, restrict the number of nitrars to one or two. The encounter works especially well if the party is traveling by boat. A nitrar swims under the craft and attempts to capsize it. If this maneuver fails, the monster exposes its head and spews a slim jet of fire to ignite the boat. The nitrar then continues it harassment until it manages to get a meal (at least one character) or it is seriously wounded.

NITRAR

AGILITY 14
Dodge 15, maneuver 15, stealth 15, swimming 15, unarmed combat 16
DEXTERITY 9
ENDURANCE 20
STRENGTH 24
TOUGHNESS 21 (25 w/armor)

INTELLECT 3
Perception 10, trick 5
MIND 3
CONFIDENCE 10
Intimidation 14, survival: swamp 14, willpower 11
CHARISMA 4
Life Points: 4
Natural Tools: Bite, damage value STR+3/27; scaly hide, armor value TOU+4/25; flame breath, range 10 meters, damage value 25.

Roleplaying Notes: Nitrars are dragon-like serpents. They have two front arms complete with razor-sharp claws, a mouth full of teeth, and scaly, rock-hard skin. Adults are fifteen meters long and three meters thick. Their skin color ranges from dull brown to murky green, allowing them to blend with their home terrain, the swamp.

GIANT SLUGS

The characters come upon a natural spring that spills into a deep, nearby pool. As soon as a character enters the water a giant slug bursts upward in a spray of water, and lunges for the unfortunate bather.

These creatures attack with almost total surprise due to their coloring and their ability to blend into the muddy bottom of a body of water.

GIANT SLUG

AGILITY 1
Stealth 4, maneuver 14 (tendrils only)
DEXTERITY 4
ENDURANCE 10
STRENGTH 10
TOUGHNESS 12
INTELLECT 1
Perception 2 (sense vibrations 14)
MIND 1
CONFIDENCE 8
Intimidation 11
CHARISMA 1
Life Points: 3
Natural Tools: Tendrils, damage value STR+1/ 11. Tendrils are used to grapple prey and drag them into the slug's mouth. If a slug gets a *good* or better success on a *maneuver* attack, it has wrapped the victim up in its sticky tendril. The victim needs to cause two wounds to the tendril (Toughness 10), or get a *good* success on a subsequent *maneuver* test. Every round after the victim is entangled, the slug tries to stuff him in its mouth, which also requires a *good* success on a *maneuver* test. Once in the slug's maw, the prey takes damage value 18 from the strong acid inside. The damage continues each round until the victim escapes or dies.

Roleplaying Notes: These slugs can reach 10 meters in length, and have long, slimy tendrils which they use to drag prey into their gigantic mouths.

QUESKWORMS

The encounter with the queskworms can occur on any type of terrain. The group comes across the rotting remains of a caravan. The wagons have been shattered as if they were tossed about by a giant of some sort. Nearby on a huge rock stands a gaunt, bedraggled man, his clothes in ruin. When he sees the party he begins to signal and wave frantically. His voice is a dry croak and his words are unintelligible. He was a member of the caravan and is trying to warn the party away. He knows that two queskworms make their homes in this area. He's safe on the rocks, but knows that the moment he steps down, he's likely to become a meal to the gigantic monsters. If the party approaches to within 50 meters of the rock, the queskworms attack.

QUESKWORM

AGILITY 9
Unarmed combat 18
DEXTERITY 5
ENDURANCE 23
STRENGTH 25
TOUGHNESS 28 (34 w/armor)
INTELLECT 4
Perception 13, tracking 13, trick 9
MIND 4
CONFIDENCE 5
Intimidation 20, survival: desert 10, willpower 19
CHARISMA 5
Life Points: 5–10 each
Natural Tools: Carapace, armor value TOU+6/ 34; mandibles, damage value STR+3/28; crushing attack, damage value STR+10/35.

Note: Queskworms are huge and powerful, but relatively slow. Above ground, their movement rate is 3; underground, the creature moves at a rate of 8. If a queskworm is about to surface, all creatures within a 100-meter radius need to make a *perception* or Intellect total of 4 or higher to notice.

Roleplaying Notes: Queskworms are highly intelligent animals, but they are overwhelmingly belligerent. It is thought that they consume all the food they need from the soil they inhabit — but that they attack convoys and large creatures because they are "trespassing" on their soil. Regardless, a queskworm will eat virtually anything it kills.

The best way to survive a queskworm attack is to run away (at least, that's the best plan anyone's ever come up with). *Trick shots* against their eye stalks look inviting, but do no actual extra damage — the queskworm is virtually blind already. Shoot or cut its eyes and you'll just piss it off.

DURAZ

This encounter is suitable for use at any gate the party travels through to reach Gwalior. A lone duraz haunts the gate and attempts to merge with a random party member.

DURAZ

AGILITY 15
Acrobatics 16, climbing 16, dodge 17, stealth 17, unarmed combat 18, unarmed parry 16
DEXTERITY 7
ENDURANCE 14
STRENGTH 15
TOUGHNESS 13 (14 w/armor)
INTELLECT 11
Perception 12, tracking 12, trick 13
MIND 6
CONFIDENCE 10
Con 22, intimidation 20, survival: Wilderness 13, willpower 12
CHARISMA 11
Charm 12, persuasion 17, taunt 15
Life Points: 3–7
Natural Tools: Scales, armor value TOU+1/14; claws, damage value STR+3/18; teeth, damage value STR+2/17

Roleplaying Notes: The duraz has the ability to lower its life processes to almost zero. A character attempting to sneak past a slumbering duraz must make a successful Agility or *stealth* total against a difficulty number equal to the creature's *perception*. Once a duraz is victorious in combat (it will try to knock its victim unconscious), its physical form crumbles and its intellect, in the form of a fine mist, possesses the host, usually entering through the mouth, nose, or ears. It then begins to regrow its physical body — it takes three months for the duraz to fully develop, although it is capable of tearing its way out of its host from two months on. While the duraz is in the body, it might simply rest until it can tear its way out, or it may try to *intimidate* or *persuade* its host to do things (like go into a city). It may also attempt to *con* its host into believing others are out to get the host, so that the host will kill and feed on fresh prey. The only way to get a duraz out of a body is to kill the body (in which case the duraz is killed) or to *persuade* or *intimidate* it into leaving. Certain magical spells may remove it in other ways, but these are the most likely "solutions."

After three months, the host will take one *wound* every day from the duraz's "stretching." These wounds will not heal. The duraz, when it kills its victim, emerges from the host's body to search for new prey.

Characters possessed by a duraz will gain the "Metabolic Difference" Compensation, since they will have to eat for two.

SCENE TWO: SLEEP OF THE DAMNED

THE SITUATION

Standard. This scene begins when the characters reach Gwalior. The once-great city has fallen into ruin. The city gates hang open, apparently destroyed from within, and hundreds, perhaps even thousands, of bodies litter the streets. The bodies are emaciated, rat-chewed, maggot-infested things, and all the more horrible because they seem to be alive, sleeping as they slip into death.

THE ACTION

A few moments after the characters enter the city, the great bell located in the highest tower in Gwalior begins to ring, evoking a deep gonging that seems to call out for lost souls.

Read aloud:

The wall separating Gwalior's capital building from the rest of the city appears to hold the only sign of life. A wan and drawn soldier calls down to you from the wall.

"Are you Tandway the sleep doctor? Oh, by the gods, it must be you. We can't hold out much longer."

Once introductions are done, the great gates leading into the capital district open, and four gaunt guards lead you to what they refer to as the Chamber of Senators. This otherwise somber room is filled with the bustle of dozens of busy magicians and doctors, all engaged in various work. Sleeping bodies cover the tables and the floor. A group of soldiers escorts you into the makeshift hospice, and Tandway immediately sets to work, telling you that your assignment is complete. You can do no more for now.

One of the four guards who escorted you here leads you to a room where you can bathe and relax for a few hours. Before leaving, he tells you that food will be sent shortly and that you'll be called for if you're needed for anything.

The guard's name is Shanus and if coaxed, he can provide the following information about the plague:

The plague began a few weeks ago. It started slowly, striking in the lower city slum areas. The number of victims seemed to grow almost exponentially. There are no symptoms; people just fall asleep and don't wake up. No external stimulus has

any effect on the slumber. It is almost as if their very souls were ripped from their mortal flesh.

At first the plague was blamed on the small Undead and Unnatural population of Gwalior. But before steps could be taken to validate that belief, the general populous took matters into their own hands, forming a lynch mob and killing thoughtlessly. In three days time there wasn't a single non-Human remaining in the city. Many went into hiding in the sewers and some escaped through the gate just before the lynching began, but most perished at the hands of the bloodthirsty mob.

When the plague didn't let up, somebody got it in their head that the spellcasters were responsible. After all, it wasn't that farfetched. Similar things have happened in other cities when some spook or other used the wrong powder or invited a creature too powerful for him to control into our world.

Martial law was declared and the surviving spell-lobbers were evacuated to the capital district, where they've been ever since.

All they've managed to figure out so far is that there's some big-league mage at work. All of them working together have been able to slow down the spread of the disease, but they still don't know what's causing it, or how to stop it.

Shanus has nothing more to tell. He leaves the characters on their own, saying that they may wander the capital district as long as they keep out of trouble. But no matter what, they may not leave for they may now be infected.

Once the characters begin to grow restless, Shanus returns to fetch them. He leads them into a small office where a disheveled and weary Tandway greets them. The somniomancer looks like he hasn't slept since he arrived.

Read aloud:

You notice a fevered gleam in Tandway's eyes as he begins to speak.

"I think I've found a solution. A cure does exist for this magical plague, but I need your help to get it." He slides a wide sheet of stone from the desk drawer. In the flickering light of an almost spent candle you can see that the stone has an unearthly green hue and that several cracks run across its surface.

"Some of the guards retrieved this for me from the cliffs bordering the ocean. This material," he tilts the stone forward for you to see better, "dates back to the Godwar. The inscriptions talk about some big-scale demon binding that happened here. I think that whatever was imprisoned here is starting to get restless.

"The problem is that this tablet doesn't tell us what it is that's bound here, or where the wards are. Someone has to go back up the cliff and find the other section of the stone. We

need to retrieve the rest of this tablet if we're to have any chance of dealing with this thing. By my estimates, everyone in this city will be dead within a week unless ..." He stares at the dusty floorboards, his shoulders slumped forward from exhaustion. Without looking up, he continues.

"Shanus and two of his guards have offered to accompany you, if you're willing. "

If the group refuses to make the trip, they are cast from the center city into the ruins to make their way back home on their own. The gamemaster should make the trip eventful, if not utterly impossible.

If the party accepts the quest, they will be outfitted with weapons and ammunition, plus any gear that they deem necessary, and that a city under siege might still have access to (gamemaster's discretion). Shanus and two guards accompany them.

SHANUS

AGILITY 10
Dodge 11, maneuver 12, melee combat 11, stealth 11, unarmed combat 12
DEXTERITY 9
Fire combat 12, vehicle piloting: wheeled 11
ENDURANCE 10
STRENGTH 10
TOUGHNESS 12
INTELLECT 9
Perception 10, tracking 11, trick 10
MIND 9
CONFIDENCE 8
Alteration: vitomancy 10, interrogation 9, intimidation 9
CHARISMA 11
Persuasion 12
Life Points: 3
Spells: *Glass jaw, slow*
Equipment: .38 Gelvash revolver; runeslugs (6) charged with mystic chains spell; blackjack; pain baton; glowstone flashlight; hand-held crystal set

GUARDS

AGILITY 8
Dodge 9, maneuver 9, melee combat 9, stealth 9, unarmed combat 9
DEXTERITY 9
Fire combat 12, thrown weapons 10
ENDURANCE 8
STRENGTH 8
TOUGHNESS 9 (11 w/armor)
INTELLECT 10
Deduction 11, perception 12
MIND 8

CONFIDENCE 8
Bribery 10, con 10, interrogation 10, intimidation 10, streetwise 9 (Gwalior 11)
CHARISMA 8
Life Points: 3
Equipment: .38 Gelvash revolver; glowstone flashlight; leather trench coat (armor value TOU+2/17)

The tablet in Tandway's possession was discovered within a cave carved out of a cliff roughly three kilometers from Gwalior. The sheer escarpment drops 100 meters to the sea below. Not much vegetation grows here since most of it was washed away by a recent tidal wave. Tandway believes that the remaining portion of the tablet can be found within a narrow chasm that splits the cliff.

The chasm extends down into the cliff for about 50 meters, gradually narrowing from two to less than a meter in width. Fortunately, the chasm runs from the edge of the cliff inward for five meters from the top all the way down to the bottom, giving the climbers room to move around. Characters must generate *climbing* totals of at least 12 to navigate the rough rock without falling.

It would be next to impossible to descend into the fissure without ropes or tools of some sort. Shanus knows this and has come prepared with a few hundred meters of rope, plus pitons and hammers. The party can split up in any fashion they desire, but Shanus advises against sending everyone into the chasm.

It proves to be good advice, since two minutes after the characters enter the chasm, the group at the top of the cliff is attacked by Zagwannorr's worshippers who seem to appear out of nowhere. These Chaos-twisted horrors seem to be a cross between normal Humans and gator-rats. There is one creature for each character in the group. Half attack from behind, while the rest scale the cliff from the water below, hoping to slay the vulnerable climbers inside the fissure.

SPAWN OF ZAGWANNORR

AGILITY 12
Climbing 15, dodge 14, stealth 15, swimming 15, unarmed combat 14
DEXTERITY 12
Fire combat 13, thrown weapons 14
ENDURANCE 9
Resist shock 11
STRENGTH 9
TOUGHNESS 10 (13 w/armor)
INTELLECT 5
Perception 8 (smell 14), trick 7
MIND 5
CONFIDENCE 9
Intimidation 10, willpower 11

CHARISMA 2
Life Points: 1
Natural Tools: The spawn of Zagwannorr are covered in a viscous slime. This is Zagwannorr's essence. When one of the creatures hits and does at least one wound damage in hand-to-hand combat, the target is subject to both a Confusion and Fear attack (see (CIV) Special Abilities in the *Bloodshadows* WorldBook for more details). The spawn have the gator-rats' scaly hide, armor value TOU+3/13 and their bite attack, damage value STR+4/13. Anytime a character takes a wound or more, he must make an Endurance roll against a base DN of 10, +1 for each wound suffered from the bite. Failure means the victim's injuries are infected, and will rot and fester until cured. Common magical healing actually traps the disease inside the flesh. The victim needs to receive better treatment before the wounds will heal. A spell that removes disease, or treatment with the *medicine* skill against a DN equal to the value above +4, is required before the character may make any healing rolls.

If the party has too easy a time, feel free to add more spawn. If, on the other hand, things are going poorly for them, have a small detachment of guards show up to lend a hand, saying that Tandway had a dream about such a danger and sent them out to assist the party. While it is important for the adventure that the party get back with the tablet, don't make it too easy for them. They should have to earn it.

SCENE THREE: UNDER THE SEA

THE SITUATION

Dramatic. This scene begins when the characters deliver the final piece of the tablet to Tandway. He fits the sections together and begins to read. After several moments, his eyes grow wide and he starts to read faster. He does not respond to anyone for ten minutes as he rereads sections of the tablet, lapses into deep thought, and then reads them again. Finally, he calls for Shanus and the remaining guards to join him and the characters. Read aloud:

"This *thing* out there is worse than I'd imagined." He looks to the tablet on the table in front of him.

"When the forces of Order and Chaos battled here during the first Godwar, a vast, unclean power was imprisoned here, and it seems that the tidal wave that hit not long ago must have weakened the seals that bind it. The tablet

tells the location of the crypt." He traces a finger across the runes until he finds the section he was looking for.

"Here. It stands several hundred meters off shore, deep under the ocean. Summon the mages, for we'll need water-breathing spells. The forces of Order bound the creature in an enchanted slumber. Since I'm the only somniomancer you've got, you have to get me out there so I can reinforce that binding spell. And we have to move fast; somehow it knows every move we make."

A deep rumble, as if it came from the core of Marl, passes through the area, making you all look to each other in wonder. From outside you here a voice shout in disbelief, "By the gods!"

THE ACTION

The sleeping bodies throughout the city have risen as one, as if some unseen puppet-master had suddenly yanked at their common string. The characters exit the Chamber of Senators to find the people plodding forward with slow, jerking steps, forming up into lines, and marching toward the sea. Tandway stumbles out behind the characters. Read aloud:

"Gods, no! We haven't any time to lose. It must have been draining the life force from these sleeping souls to feed its strength. It's calling them to it, so it can feed on their flesh! We must leave immediately!"

"It must be trying to snuff them out all at once to give it the boost in power it needs to break free! The guards must prevent their escape from the city while we go on ahead and try to reestablish the wards that keep the Lord of Chaos down."

The marching sleepers do nothing other than walk unless someone or something tries to block their progress. If that happens, they attack with a base *unarmed combat* score of 10, doing damage value 10. If left to their own again, they stop attacking and begin to march.

BATTLE UNDER THE SEA

If the party's magicians can't come up with enough *water-breathing* spells for everyone, the surviving magicians in Gwalior can cast them. The trip beneath the waves to the underwater crypt is uneventful. Once the group gets within 1,000 meters of the huge, moss-covered structure, beings begin to erupt from the slimy, silt-covered floor of the ocean. These creatures may have at one time been normal sea creatures, but the years of proximity to

Zagwannorr have warped them. There are three creatures which at one time might have been squids, a giant amorphous blob which could have been a jellyfish, and several half-Human, half-fish creatures wielding spears made of coral. All have a palpable aura of decay and death. The children of Chaos burst forth from their confinement and attack.

FISH CREATURES (10)
AGILITY 10
Dodge 12, melee combat 11, swimming 13, unarmed combat 11
DEXTERITY 13
Thrown weapons 15
ENDURANCE 8
STRENGTH 10
TOUGHNESS 10 (12 w/armor)
INTELLECT 6
Perception 7, trick 7
MIND 5
CONFIDENCE 7
CHARISMA 2
Life Points: 1
Natural Tools: Thick hide, armor value TOU+2/12
Equipment: Coral spear, damage value STR+3/13

SQUID CREATURES (3)
AGILITY 9
Dodge 10, swimming 12, unarmed combat 11
DEXTERITY 8
ENDURANCE 11
Resist shock 12
STRENGTH 10
Lifting 12
TOUGHNESS 11 (14 w/armor)
INTELLECT 5
MIND 6
CONFIDENCE 7
Intimidation 91
CHARISMA 4
Life Points: 1
Natural Tools: Thick hide, armor value TOU+3/14; four tentacles, crushing damage value STR+10/20

JELLYFISH CREATURE
AGILITY 7
Swimming 9, unarmed combat 10
DEXTERITY 8
ENDURANCE 12
STRENGTH 11
TOUGHNESS 12
INTELLECT 7
Perception 9
MIND 6

CONFIDENCE 6
CHARISMA 3
Life Points: 1
Natural Tools: Stinging flagella, damage value STR+8/19, stung characters must generate an Endurance total of at least 15 or else succumb to the paralyzing poison injected by the jellyfish creature, which renders the characters immobile for three rounds.

After the battle, Tandway attempts to restore the binds holding Zagwannorr in check. Read aloud:

Through the veils of blood that have slowly begun to mix with the salty ocean water, you can see Tandway swimming frantically toward a huge slab of metal half-buried in the sea floor.

When he gets within a few meters he stops and starts gesturing. As the water clears, you realize that the slab is actually a giant metal box inscribed with runes and other indecipherable markings.

Suddenly, with a deep boom, the box rocks, throwing sand and seaweed up and around it. Tandway disappears behind the forming cloud.

All goes silent.

When the cloudy water clears, you see Tandway lying on top of the huge box.

Tandway gave his own life force to power the spell needed to re-seal Zagwannorr's tomb. Unfortunately for him, the Chaos Lord contacted him as his spirit left his body, telling him she would come after his soul when she freed herself from the bonds of Order.

AFTERMATH

The characters return to Gwalior after their battle with Zagwannorr's minions. Read aloud:

Just as you get within sight of Gwalior, the city's main gates burst open and hundreds of people pour out. As they come closer you can hear their cheers and calls of thanks. The swarm engulfs you, lifting you onto their shoulders and carrying you back into the city.

The celebration rages all night, and some of it you do not remember. Early the next morning, a note slides under your door. It reads:

"OvEr NOt
oVEr nOT
shE LiVEs
YOu Die
cHAos WiNS"

No other messages come to you for the rest of the day, leaving you to ponder the meaning of the strange words, and what effect they might possibly have on your lives.

AWARDS

All surviving characters receive three skill points each. Also, characters may be awarded 1–3 Life Points depending on the outcome of the adventure.

CHAPTER SEVEN

BORN IN BLOOD

A Tale of the First Godwar by Daniel Scott Palter

The first Godwar was like a flawed conjurestone. Everyone saw in it what they wanted to …

— Hieronymus East

She sat daintily before the fire, pecking at a slice of liver from her erstwhile lover. She made such a pretty picture, the youngest and most animated of my current crop of child tribute-brides. Wise beyond her years, every gesture and expression was timed for maximum effect. She only betrayed her youth in forgetting how truly old I was. Still, at her age, it was easy to confuse a man's indulgence of her schemes and whims for the lust-besotted blindness of an ancient geezer.

The lover who was not to be turned slowly on the spit over the open flames. The skin had been shaved and patiently scrubbed. Now the fat and blood dripped onto the flames with an endless petty current of hisses and bubbles. He should have been dead or at least in shock. He wasn't that lucky. Hadn't occurred to him that a mage strong enough to be a lifetaker at distance could also be a life and consciousness prolonger. Hadn't occurred to him also that the very character traits that had let him rise to be one of my most trusted guardsmen so rapidly were the ones which made him so transparent as a conspirator. Hint: mages who live for centuries do not do so by letting guileful people with weapons close to them. Live and learn, die in despair. He did, he was.

The hilltop brightened with moonrise. Flat and barren, it sat almost deserted except for the fire and ourselves. My guards were deployed discretely around the slopes. The few officers with us announced their presence before cresting the top on their rounds. The not quite lover's transition from watch captain to roast had led to some rapid promotions and a healthy new level of fearful respect for what a nasty mage I could be when one attracted my attention.

Three of my leather-winged familiars flitted back and forth between the picket line and the fire, carrying fresh snacks in bite-sized nuggets. Think of it as character building for the ambitious. Out here in the outback, a position as mage's guard was a big step up for a young tribesman or bandit of whatever species. Tonight's entertainment was causing many their first pause to consider the source and price of their more splendid existence.

Mike Vilardi

Mighty mages are supposed to be in cities with runewarded palaces and staffs of thousands at their beck and call. I had dwelled seemingly forever in the back end of nowhere, content to take tribute from the few poor dwellers of this lowly collection of hills, steppes and canyons. Wealth they had seen. Its source seemed a mystery. Over the centuries stories of me as a mighty mage from elsewhere and when had slowly faded before other tales of a former great one in hiding, slowly paying out his storehouse of treasures. The events of the last few days had prompted some reconsideration but little real comprehension. All the better for me. The fewer who understood techlegging or darktrading the better for me in the days to come.

She paused in her nibbling to look up at me, her large violet eyes gazing on me with rapt attention. It was an expression and look she'd practiced long and hard before the mirror in her room when she was away from me. She fancied it kept me enthralled with her charm.

She did it well. Given a bit more practice she might get as good at it as her grandmother had been. She was seventh in training in a line of child bride to tribal wise woman of her clan. Having been father to each, I took a very proprietary interest in the development.

"Tell me a story," she lilted. Her voice was like music.

"You've heard most of them. At least the ones which would make any sense to you," I answered.

"Please. Any of the ones of how you came to be here."

We had hours to wait till the dragon star crested the horizon just before dawn. A story would pass the time as easily as a snack. Besides, my son, carried so hugely inside her barely beyond child's frame, would need to learn it all eventually anyway …

It was long ago and far away. No, don't think of years and miles. It was another where, another when. You could journey across all the stars you see and never come to where I started. Journey back across the years of this universe and never find the one I began in. There are many universes, many wheres and many whens. With the right powers or the right tools or a bit of each, doors, gates, passages can be opened between them. Where this was is so many gates away that the concepts are meaningless.

Anyway, it was my first body, my first life. I was not yet a mage and had no dreams of being one. By my reckoning, I was a mature man of rising wealth and no little skill. The world I was born to was a world of men.

None of the near and not so near men that inhabit our current homeplace existed there. It was a bigger world—giant continent, even larger seas, huge polar wastes. Many men grouped in a clusters of squabbling kingdoms, petty theocracies and city states with vast, loosely claimed and even more loosely settled wastes between them. I was a caravan trader roaming these wastes — trading for the two scarcest things this large world had, metal and magic.

The metal shortage has something to do with the world's size. Bigger the world the less metal it has or something like that. Settled areas had been mined out long ago. The wastes turned up nuggets, seams, little mines worked by clans with their family forts at the minehead, herder clans who prospected and panned on the side or in the winter grazing range. They wanted settled goods but wouldn't deal with borders, and guards, and tariffs and all the ways settled men have of cheating the outlander while hiding behind laws. So that left traders like me who roamed the outback for months or years, buying and selling.

Area I roamed was a triangle of wastelands and steppes between three settled zones. Not enough water or grass to support a real army marching from one to the other. The zoners were relatively few, scattered and of little account. They seldom troubled to raid even the fringes of the settled zones, so great was their inferiority in numbers and weapons. So except for a very occasional punishment raids to make sure that the zone stayed unsettled and disunited, the settled folk left them pretty much alone. Caravans like mine, with clan connections on each of the three sides, paid their border fees and taxes outbound and inbound but didn't get fleeced like a zoner did. Manufactures and luxuries went out. Metal, handiworks, furs and herds came back. Guards never knew when or if an outbound caravan would be back. A lot died in the zone. A number stayed there, one reason or another. Of those that were left, they could go back or keep going to either end of the triangle. Long and the short of it was, as long as the caravan leader's clan was known and would stand surety, the guards would pretty much accept that whoever came out of the zone with a caravan had a right to.

Now I wasn't born to this clan. This was a settled world. Most folk liked things as they were — didn't want to go into the zones, leave comforts behind, take risks. Wild and free were bad. A place for everything and everything striving to better itself only within settled mores and customs. So even clans of traders and travelers had problems getting the kids to do the 'in the zone' part of the business or keeping the older ones at it. Made these clans very open to swaps, cross adoptions, call it what you will. They took other clans problems off their hands, threw them out in the zone in the next caravan and saw what floated or sank.

Me, I was trouble to my birth clan from the day I was born. Not big things. Little ones but never-

ending. Like I was out to lunch the day they explained to everyone else how the world worked, what was right and wrong, what was and wasn't done or said. I asked the wrong questions, laughed at the wrong parts of the joke, I was some changeling in any setting of more than one person. Why deal with it when you can get some trader clan kid whose elders would add a bit of a sweetener to the deal. So off I went on my first trek and got my first taste of magic. Wasn't supposed to but I did.

Settled region I grew up in, the priests had most all of the magic and pretty much ran things, either directly or through whoever the local noble or warlord was. Wasn't even a separate class of mages or warlocks or whatever. This was pretty much the same throughout the continent and across most of the vast ocean's isles.

What few local witches there were, the priests burned them when they caught them. So normal folk didn't have magic for doorseals or firestarters or much of anything. Those that had the power liked to keep it that way. The few who had other magic kept it very hidden — their death was only one informer away. Made magic, especially the chaotic or black sorts, rare and expensive. Most of those who sold it sold fake — smoke and mirrors. The real stuff went for big prices if you knew where and how.

Me, I knew neither at first. Just knew there had to be more to life than what I saw. Six months into the zone of fetch and tote, guard and scurry, I'd begun to get my first clues on how to trade. Sounds easy — buy low, sell high. The trick is buy what, sell where? I was barely old enough to bargain and had little enough to trade from. Beside, sidetrading was, if not forbidden by the clan, at least roughly discouraged, so I needed to pick my opportunities carefully. The trick therefore had to be size. Small and novel, relying on newness for value.

So I'd gotten into the habit of swapping camp shifts for scout and flanker work. It was an easy trade. My lack of social skills was notable even in this collection of misfits and weirdos that passed for a trading clan. I'd made it into none of the cliques, even into the newbie cliques. Hadn't really tried that hard — social failure was a lesson I'd already learned. Spent all my efforts on mastering the skills needed on trek. You see none of us newbies knew anything, so that great lecture on "how things worked" that I'd missed back in town for once didn't matter. Out of fifty or so newbies who'd started this trek more than half were gone by now — dead, maimed and abandoned, lost, run away, sold as slaves to some passing fortlet because the clan had already written them off as hopeless. I wasn't of any real worth to them yet, but I'd passed my first few cullings and was one of the few newbies that didn't scare older and wiser heads when sent off to do outside work.

Figuring was that I was already good enough to at least make noise dying, so I'd serve my purpose while I got in some more on the job training.

Yeah, it was dangerous but a snake could get you in camp easy as an arrow, or a big cat off by yourself. A very little skill, the balls of a brass fertility idol and a lot of luck were all any of us newbies had at this point. Like fish swimming upstream to spawn, a great many stiffs to get a few winners. But what it gave me was occasions when I tripped over some zoner who had stuff to trade but didn't fancy coming into camp. I'd already found two older traders to work with. I'd meet the loners, take the risk of the approach, come out next shift with what they wanted and make the swaps. If it was a big enough deal my two "partners" would come with me. Some of it went into the clan store and some they held out. I hadn't learned yet how the protocol on that one went so my holdouts were solo deals I could do on the spot. Made me very aggressive in my scouting.

Anyway, it was a late afternoon. Not dusk but definitely shadows from both suns. I came over a ridgeline out to the flank and rear of the caravan. Rolling steppe country where a hundred foot rise could take a mile, so a ridge like this was worth sitting on for the view. I was armed but all sharpened stone and ceramics, no metal. Newbies don't rate metal. Made me cold meat for anyone with bronze much less steel. Trick was to see and evade. Ridge made me visible but made for great vision in return.

So when the mule I was riding spooked cresting, I reigned in. Figured it was easily twice my age and probably saw, heard, or sensed something I didn't. Was frantically scanning every dip and rock for predators or bandits when I felt it too. Hairs on my body started standing up. Weird feeling in my head. Shimmer in my eyes.

Any other newbie would have screamed and ran at that point. I'd already learned that mistake. Eyes see motion better than objects. Nudged the mule back into shadow while I waited. Sky parted — didn't know any better way to describe it then. A black hole in the air maybe half way down the slope, then a glimpse of somewhere else thru the hole, then suddenly there was a lady and a thing that hadn't been there before.

Mule about freaked but I clubbed it good upside the head. This was every clan mother's scare tale about Chaos magic and Demons from hell. The thing had more claws and teeth and eyes than I wanted to think about. The woman wore a strange thick bulky cloth one piece garment like nothing I'd ever seen or heard of and carried more weapons than a pack of raiders. If they wanted me dead, running wasn't probably going to help.

She carried a long thing that looked vaguely like a crossbow, which could surely reach me before I crested again. Even beyond that I didn't really think that my mule was going to outrun the thing.

Put the club back in its scabbard. Left my hands on the reins in *very* plain sight. Waited. Thing bounded past me over the ridge in an obvious scout/lookout position. She came walking up covering me with the long thing. As she got closer it became obvious that the long thing didn't have a bolt or any sort of string. Had a hole at the end and a trigger. Didn't know how it worked. Wasn't planning to find out if I could help it.

She gets in close and gives me a good once over.

I'm keeping very still, respectful like. She wants meat, I'm dead. I play the odds that she didn't need to get into spitting distance to fetch dinner. Wait for the pitch.

First surprise, she talks to the thing, not me. Long whistle, followed by a short one. Thing bounds back and takes up a flank position, so if I go for my crossbow I can only aim at one of them. Yeah. Sure. Shadows getting deeper. First moon rising, started to block second sun.

Second surprise — the thing does the talking. It didn't move its many mouths. But it projected words into my head … yes, I know you can do that. Yes, it's a child's trick for serious magic users of our kind. Remember that I was a child and in many ways far less knowledgeable than you are now. You come from a long line of wise women. You've had magic around you all your life. You've shared bed and board with a mage. All I knew is that priests could do strange things and Demons would eat your soul. Very morally uplifting and all that but scarcely much to go on for practical magics.

Anyway, the next surprise was no threats. I had expected to be threatened body and soul, forced to do foul things and who knows what else. Instead I was offered a bribe. A fine steel dagger and a dozen steel tipped quarrels for my crossbow merely to perform a small package delivery. What was in the package? My most important decision was made at that moment. I didn't know and didn't choose to ask. You cannot blurt out what you don't know.

So that early evening I got "lost" from my caravan.

Six weeks later I ride slowly out of the steppe straight up to the proper border post at another end of the triangle , salute the guard with a gift of fresh meat and ask to have my clan house notified. Gave them a plausible newbie story about getting lost. Gave them a parcel of trade goods I'd accumulated along the way. Hid the package down my pants.

Wasn't a long wait till my clan sent a party to fetch me. They searched my saddle bags carefully, confiscated the mule and two extra donkeys I'd accumulated along the way for the clan house, and beat the shit out of me for being a newbie screwup. After which they lost interest in me for a few days while trying to figure out what to do with me.

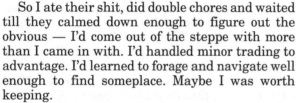

Mike Vilardi

So I ate their shit, did double chores and waited till they calmed down enough to figure out the obvious — I'd come out of the steppe with more than I came in with. I'd handled minor trading to advantage. I'd learned to forage and navigate well enough to find someplace. Maybe I was worth keeping.

Didn't do anything the first two times I was let out of clan house. Let whoever they and the guard had assigned to tail me follow me through the market and back while I ate some new things, watched whatever was free and generally acted like a newbie in a city and culture I'd never seen before. Didn't flash money or metal. No one tried to talk to me.

By the end of a half moon I was yesterday's news. Talk was focused on yet another minor war in this end of settled reality. Sudden need for meat. I'd come in with meat. Must have some hunting skills as a newbie with stone weapons …

"But you said you were given steel … "

Don't interrupt. I wasn't stupid enough to bring steel anywhere near the border. Buried it carefully two hills down the road and far enough off the trail where I could presume they'd keep for a while. Anyway, by now I was assigned to a new caravan to be sent back in on a quick trade for cured meat or herd beasts of any sort. Night before we were to

leave the whole group went out on the town. Not the total newbies of course, but I'd been through it once and had been asked for by name by the trek leader. Wasn't hard to pour more of my drinks on the floor than down my throat. Made like the virgin I was and ran when it got from drinking to wenching.

No tails but I was cautious anyway. Many nasty things in a strange town besides the watch go stirring after true dark. But I knew where I was going — weeks on the trail had been enough to memorize the mark on the sign before I'd burned the paper it had been sketched on. So say an hour before final moonrise I'm in an old general trail goods store near the main gate steppewards.

Places like this open early as every party wants to be on gateline by first light. So I seem right at home spending what little I had on some private trade goods for the trail. Had to wait till the right clerk was free. Had to ask for a strange but not expensive list of things in a particular order. O.K., either I wind up inside the temple guards dungeon now or I've done it right. Didn't know enough to be smart yet, but the luck was still with me. The lady had given me a charm that the thing said would protect me up to a point. Multicolored animal tooth on a rawhide thong. The sort of stupid thing a newbie would trade for thinking it was valuable. It looked strange and different from anything I'd ever seen before. However, any experienced trekker would make it for a common tooth of a medium steppe cat, an item of absolutely no commercial value. Took the package out of my pants with my pouch. Slid it across the counter and turned to go about my business.

Made it out the door and got the tap on the shoulder.

Stopped and looked. No temple guards. No watchmen.

No clan elders with big clubs. Three of them, normal looking. Claimed to be friends of my birthclan. Insisted on buying me a snack. Spent more time than I'd care to remember grilling me on years old clan gossip that I was mostly inventing on the spot. Insisted on walking me back to my clan house. Dangerous streets you know. Not a word that anyone could peg as wrong. Just a most unlikely chance encounter. With three very average men who I could never identify in a crowd, who happened to be walking down the street with a long lost chum when up steps my trek leader and his two favorite goons.

I play dumb and introduce everybody. Only they already know each other. Large hands around my arms and over my mouth. Shoved through a doorway into a packing warehouse. The six of them take turns beating the shit out of me all over again. Only this time the questions are a lot more to the point. What did I bring out? Who gave it to me? What did I see? I don't bother thinking up lies. Just scream with the pain and wait to die. It seems to go on several lifetimes. Shifts from pain to rape to water into my lungs and stomped out again to a red hot bronze knife blade. Final act is they smack me awake so I can watch them yank out one of my canine teeth with a cold pair of pliers.

Suddenly it's over. I'm out for what seems to be a million years but is maybe two days. I wake up with a hood being yanked off over my head in the back of a small wagon. We're parked off the road maybe two hills from the guard post. By a hole in the ground. My little metal treasures are spread out in front of me. I wait for the questions to start again. They don't. The three long lost "friends" and the trek leader are gone. The two goons take turns talking. They basically tell me what happened. Not my woman warrior and thing. Strange people, stranger things, gods, Demons, light and dark and chaos.

I find out that I'm not the first courier to crawl out of the wastes. Not the tenth either. Trek leader's part of a clique/cult/subclan that's being doing this kind of thing for generations. Get a compliment for the hiding place. Took them a day to find it …

"You must have been very brave!!!" she pipes in with. The proper line for such a situation and she usually responds on cue. My way of knowing she's still vaguely awake. Moon's down. Dragon star still over the horizon. Time for a bit more of a story she's heard in various bits and pieces since her mother's clan made its pilgrimage to the mage's citadel to leave their new tribute bride.

She'd been such a bold little one, brushing my two then favorites out of their normal bed rotation within half a moon. Had herself mistress of the house in a half year. Not easy to pull on a pack of jealous other wives who have you on size and experience. Yet again, they all seemed to ignore that I ever had anything to do with the results. Apparently mages could move mountains but were putty in the hands of their wenches and staff. Yeah. Sure …

Brave had little to do with it. Figured myself for dead either way once it started. Had a better chance on a quick death from too much anger in the blows than a slow death trying to keep my lies straight. Fact was I knew damn near nothing. But once I admitted anything, there'd be more sessions to get the "rest" out of me and I had no "rest" to sell."

Anyway, they were semi-gentle with me after the discussion. Pain/sleep potions whenever I woke and a good quilt to lie in while the wagon ate miles catching the caravan. Catching and then passing it turned out. My next clear memory, we're maybe three days ahead. Camped at a muddy ford of a slow wide stream. Good base to meet herders with beasts to trade. Gives us a good excuse to be there ahead of the trek.

My new patron brings me awake with a good smack then stands me up on a wagon for the group to see. His people; some herder tribesmen who seem very well acquainted with him; a few of the youngest, smallest newbies and some equally small and helpless castoffs from the clan's kitchen skuts/slaves/hangers on; a scattered bunch I cannot yet place, all different in twos and threes — maybe 60–75 folks all told, two-thirds partyers and one-third skut staff/sex objects of either gender. Party time and I'm the guest of honor. Drinks and drugs and sex, single and group, but that's all side happening. Folks just seem happy to see each other, lot of gossip and back slapping. Not like any parties I've ever seen, kid or adult. More like the trekkers quarter on a warm summer's night.

Anyway, the big guy — call him Kurt, it's as close to the real one as our language has — is singing my praises as his best new pupil/protege. Passed my initiation by not talking despite certain death, blah, blah, blah. Mainly I'm "in" with whatever "in" there is here. Yeah, sure, whatever he says. I'm just trying to keep my head up which isn't easy as I'm seeing six of him and hearing maybe nine.

Tribal woman comes up front. Wearing lots of charms, amulets, tattooed with strange symbols around the neck, ankles and both wrists. Starts

Mike Vilardi

keening a chant in something not altogether Human and the clan goes real still. Takes up my lucky charm and bites it. The sound it produces was beyond hearing. Horses and camels snort and scream. Most of the assembly goes still except for a few who join her chant. Sky's gone dark.

Everyone who isn't chanting is pressing forward, the grownups dragging the newbies and skuts who suddenly are trying to make themselves very small. Hair on my neck's going up again. Shimmer all across the sky. Flash bang, big time and there's two ladies and four things. Witch woman and her little group are chanting atonally, half of it seeming beyond the range of Human hearing or speech. Everyone else is being very respectful.

Kurt has four little ones dragged up to me, two of each. "Choose" one he bellows. I grab some kitchen skut so badly beaten she looks like a slab of raw roast. Maybe she was the smallest. Maybe she was the closest. All I was concentrating on was "doing something."

He takes the first newbie boy, strips him in like nothing flat and throws him to the things. Feeding time — slow, very formal dance as they pick him to pieces bite by bite. Crowd's cheering. Two ladies walk up to the second newbie …

I can see her start to drift. Good. At her age an endless tale of blood and mayhem may be amusing. You don't begin to know how old it gets by my age.

Besides most of the blood is bullshit anyway. Chaos magic always attracts its share of hellraisers and sociopaths. The sort of people who think butchering helpless skuts makes heros out of them. My kind were the serious subversives. We paid our temple offerings, kept out of trouble, and were content to work in slow time.

Take me and my little skut. We formed a fast partnership that night amid the cannibal feast. I got her a healing potion. I tended her wounds. I didn't become the nth owner to screw her, grope her, shove a wagon whip down her throat or up her ass. How terribly unmanly of me. Really wasn't all that worried about my horrible urges getting satisfied someday. I was playing a different game. Starting a sub-subclan of two. Gratitude and empathy are a far better coin to buy loyalty than fear. Someone/something else can always be scarier than you. But when hope is gone and you give it back, it touches places that not even pain or the fear of death can reach. Little Brown Eyes, as I renamed the skut, would die for, kill for me, do what I say and watch my back. A big start to my true future.

Not that anybody noticed amid all the other fireworks and high jinks. I got noticed once more when I got grabbed for my first two implants. Nail driven into my jaw, right where my knocked out tooth had been. Grew into a lovely fake canine in about 80 seconds. My first object of power. And then, just to make sure I'd be a good little Chaos boy someone made a cut on the back of my neck and they fed in a brain worm. Lovely little parasite. gave me my first "powers," symbiotically of course. Guarantee of a painful death if the temple guard found it. Symbiote was sensitive to certain sorts of white magic. If it died, would take my brain and me with it.

After my "worming" the party went back to normal.

About true dawn I got Brown Eyes up and we drifted over to one of the things. Started to have a little talk. I wanted back in the courier business but from a different angle. Sure, we'd run packages. But what we wanted wasn't metal. Wasn't anything you could see. We wanted knowledge. Tools at first — the magic came later.

Metal I can only sell once. But tech can be resold over and over before it becomes general knowledge. Especially if you sell it in pieces without context.

Nothing that attacked the temples directly. Purely economic stuff in the beginning. A slightly better way to refine ores that I must have sold to half a thousand clan mines before word got out. How to get a really good cutting edge on a special ceramic you could use for leather cutting — almost as good as metal and less than 1/10th the price. Always able to say it came from the far side of the zone. Often able to trade my new bit for special pieces of clan knowledge that could then in turn be resold.

Brown Eyes and I built our group carefully. Simply seemed to be the deadbeats of Kurt's group. But word spread. More of our newbies lived than any other group.

Slaves and skuts could get promoted freedman with us. Always kicked back to Kurt and clan. There was always enough to go around. Never a pile to be seized or counted. Loans out, money working to make money. Favors owed.

Twenty years passed. The clan split and then split again. Kurt was now overlord of a megaclan of the best and boldest trekkers. Brown Eyes and I ran a very prosperous subclan with our own subclanhouses in every major trading city of the three settled zones plus quite a few in the zone fortlets and base camps.

She never forgot being saved that night. She was going to prove herself worthy, which she did. On the surface the most meticulous house mother/administrator you could imagine. Never took a steady lover, never minded when I did. All efficiency and training and supervision. Under the surface, the best private spymaster in all the clans. Ran a triple level system across multiple cities through very carefully groomed subordinates and surprise inspections. Outer level was an utterly loyal ring who knew nothing of what went on in the zone and just saw a very shrewd trading clan in an era of ever more rapid growth and change. Supposed inner level knew a great deal more, all of it wrong and contained priests' and watch spies galore. Completely hidden among the two was the actual gang. Each personally recruited, trained and screened by my ever so thorough Brown Eyed co-conspirator.

We specialized in in-city delivery, pickup, and surveillance but had a still deeper core group that did theft, murder, and hexing. Recruited from those with a grudge against the priests in particular and the world in general. Twenty years and they never took one alive. Rarely took one with enough intact to investigate. So the trails died in the undercities … and we were safe … for a while …

Twenty years of preparation for what the things told us had to come next, the war finally coming to us. Happened on a day when my partner and I were in the same clanhouse, on her birth side of the steppe, not mine. Very convenient but pure chance. It pays to be lucky.

Like my first day on the ridge but 10,000 times stronger. Blasted everyone on the planet awake and terrified. The sky was in pieces and the archangels were descending from the heavens. Maybe half the priests on the planet died that morning — of heresy, of pride, to make examples, to settle scores. All the groups like Kurt's went in the next week. Already ratted out, sold out by the likes of us, too obvious in what they did, too prideful to walk under the new yoke.

Left us with a planetary theocracy, run by the direct representatives of heaven. The gods needed ever more drafts of soldiers and ever higher taxes to send to fight the Demon threat beyond the sky. Us, we were loyal temple stooges. Geeked from minute one. Hid what we could and cauterized the rest before the trails could reach us. Let the war take its course. There was plenty of time. We'd been pegged by our internal spies as gutless money chasers … no real threat. Besides once a war gets going, technology suddenly seems part of the war effort.

Inherited Kurt's contacts in the zone. Sold a steady stream of the crazies to the priests. Kept the good ones for ourselves. Five years of ever higher taxes, ever greater drains of war production, endless press gangs of "volunteers" for good being sent off elsewhere to die. Strange people and stranger things passing through, with some of them based or left here.

The theocracy strains under the changes. Schisms and rebellions. Conspiracies and plots. Informers and self-promoters everywhere. Holy men calling out against the changes, screaming to heaven against a war we never sought and could barely understand. Judgment day was coming and we'd been bad little beings …

The war goes even more badly. Sabotage and raids on us within our system and through ever more gates and pathways. Monsters and things creeping out of shadows. Night becomes terrible and the zone ever less safe.

New riders coming out of the zone with each caravan and trek. Demanding sanctuary. Demanding supplies.

Brown Eyes copes somehow but we are strained. Only my constant machinations keeps us safe, but definitely not above suspicion.

Finally it all comes tumbling down. The war reaches us. Dreadful magics in the sky day and night as assemblies of rival mages contend for our skies. Colors beyond color. Sound beyond sound. Battle joined above our heads and inside our hearts.

The temple troops herd us all into the squares around the temples. We've congregated our best secret cadre and the fiercest new guests in a knot. At a sign from one we strike. Sixty temple guards cut down in the merest instant. Exploded heads, ruptured innards, slit throats, there are a thousand ways to die. But in the end all the same — fear, blood , pain, death. Very graphic, very fast. My few favored tame priests open the gates and in we bound. Three mages chant us a gate and the legions of Yusef, the berserkers of Saer, Ison's acolytes — call them what you will, pour through. Half the world dies in a night of blood and fire, death and damnation. Archangels fall before fanged, winged demons. Judgment day. The new dawn,

We'd won. And I was lost …

Sleepy head lifts her eyes a bit. Too tired for the practiced expressions. "How lost? You won? What did you lose? Your powers? Your woman? Your gold?"

"Pacts with Demons are rarely that simple. We were their best performing team. They offered enhanced powers, new bodies, new lives, immortality, demi-godhood, wealth and adventure, new worlds to conquer, anything and everything … that's how I wound up here."

"This is defeat?"

"You're young. Younger than I was. It all sounded grand and getting rid of the brain worm sounded grander. Brown Eyes tried to tell me. Half the world dead before Judgment Day. Half again dead in a night. Alive was better. Entrench yourself with the new powers that be. Crawl into a very safe hole and let the war pass you buy. We'd both wagered body and soul once, why risk it to double the bet? Let the gods fight their own war."

"She was unworthy of you. I'll be the mistress of your new days of glory … !!! Aeiyyech!!!"

Poor little child. She would be the mother of my new glory, not its mistress. I had followed the star road across the gates and times until at Marl I found myself stranded on a beachhead that wasn't going to be supported in a war Heaven had lost interest in. The gates were slammed shut behind us. A lucky few withdrew in time to somewhere somewhen a bit closer home. The rest of us were left to wait, to rot, to hide, to discover that Little Brown Eyes was right all along. Once you are on top, alive is better than dead and the rest is ashes …

"Aeiyyehheh!!!!" Her scream could tear the heart from a gargoyle. The Demon had risen. Soon the gate would begin to form. An even louder scream cascaded from her writhing body. A foot-long claw extended from her distended belly. My son, the child of the Demon soul I harbored inside this Human form, slit her from neck to crotch in one deft stroke. His scaly body wriggled out with a mouthful of intestine in his leathery beak. He fixed his three eyes on me and began to feed as his wings flexed behind him, drying in the light of the new gate to the star road. I am content …

CHAPTER EIGHT

VOYAGE OF THE DOOMED

SCENE ONE: ALL ABOARD

THE SITUATION

Standard. The characters, for their own reasons, board the tramp steamer *Jolly Marie*, bound from Galitia to the city of Dela. The boarding and launch takes place at night from the docks in the Esler district.

As the adventure begins, hand out notes or index cards to the players with the reason their characters are boarding the ship. The characters may or may not know each other — and it doesn't really matter who gets which card, unless noted. Here are some possible reasons for leaving Galitia:

You're wanted for murder — well, you weren't going to stand for being cheated. This steamer is a convenient mode of escape until the city cools off. Watch out for law on board.

You're being paid well to smuggle a conjurestone out of the city. You're not sure what it contains — you've been warned not to watch it — just hand it over to the fence when you get to Dela. (GM Note: The vid is of a Galitian City Elder in a compromising position — actually a series of compromising positions — with twin 'Shifters.)

You were involved in an ill-fated affair with Fantasia Ell, the girlfriend of Arle, a prominent gangster. Three breeds, each roughly the size of a truck, "suggested" you leave town ... now.

You are working undercover for the Alchemists' Guild, looking into the smuggling of alchemical components to Dela.

You are a minor member of an infamous Chaos cult in Galitia. Lately, membership's been dropping ... dead. You decided it might be healthier elsewhere. (This one should only go to a character with a Chaotic alignment.)

You're running away ... from your job, your family, everything. You just want to start fresh, somewhere else, and you're willing to risk the waters of the Skorn to get there.

THE ACTION

Read aloud or paraphrase:

There's a cold wind on the docks tonight that cuts through you like a rusty knife. You stand amid a knot of strangers, all of you lost in your own thoughts. Stevedores are loading boxes of cargo on the steamer, some large, some small. Until they're done, passengers aren't allowed on board. Directing the operation is the *Jolly Marie*'s captain, Wolf Largo.

The characters should be somewhat at loose ends, all of them anxious to get going and not able to get on board just yet. It's doubtful that any will offer to help load the cargo, but if they do, they are turned down flat, and Larson will probably bark at them to go back and wait with the other passengers.

After a few moments, a few of the characters notice some attractive members of the opposite sex standing on the pier near the edge of the water. They appear to be waiting to board as well, and flash smiles. Having nothing else to do, the characters might well decide to go over and strike up some conversation.

This would be a bad thing, because these aren't Humans — they're tangalor tentacles, part of a Wilderness creature native to the waters around Galitia. And it's in the mood for a midnight snack …

TANGALORS

Tangalors make their homes in the Skorn. They have thick, awkward cigar-shaped bodies formed from tightly woven layers of plant fibers. They spend most of their time secured to some large underwater rock or other stabilizer, using two or three of their nine extraodinarily long kelp tentacles interlaced with tiny, fibrous eyestalks, to anchor themselves.

Once in position, tangalors normally hunt at night, snaking between three and six of their tentacles into the air to use as lures for their victims. A tangalor's tentacles have a slightly hallucinogenic effect, causing victims to see something alluring. Once a tangalor can lure a victim to within a meter or so of its tentacle, the creature will lash out with its other strands in an attempt to drag the poor sap underwater to his doom.

Tangalors will not attack Vampires, Undead or Zombies.

STANDARD TANGALOR

AGILITY 8
Stealth 10, unarmed combat 13
DEXTERITY 5
ENDURANCE 11
Resist shock 13

STRENGTH 13
Lifting 14
TOUGHNESS 11
INTELLECT 9
Perception 12, trick 11
MIND 5
CONFIDENCE 9
Intimidation 14, survival: underwater 12, willpower 15
CHARISMA 5
Life Points: 3
Natural Tools: Multiple eyestalks (Special Abilities (CIII): Multiple Abilities I — +1 to perception attempts that negate surprise; ability to appear as a welcome or attractive figure (Special Abilities (CIV): Natural Sorcery I — the illusions cast using this ability can be disbelieved with an Intellect or perception total of 7; tentacles allow creature to make up to three single attacks per round without incurring multi-action penalty.

Note: Tangalors will not move from their position unless *heavily wounded*.

Assuming the characters aren't wary of these attractive types, the tangalor should get initiative in the first round of combat. The first interesting question is, if some of the characters get attacked, will the others go help? It's by no means a certainty — but some of the sailors will go to their aid. One of the ones who does will be carrying a crate marked with a red rune in the shape of a serpent, which he drops when he rushes to help. Larson will immediately begin screaming at him to "forget those idiots and bring that crate aboard!"

Remember that, although there is only one tangalor, he's hidden beneath the murky waters of the Skorn, so the characters will likely be fighting his tentacles. If sufficient damage is done to those, the tangalor will dislodge itself from its hiding place and float further down the river to hunt again.

CAPTAIN WOLF LARGO

AGILITY 9
Climbing 10, dodge 12, melee combat 12, melee parry 11, swimming 11, unarmed combat 11, unarmed parry 11
DEXTERITY 9
Fire combat 12, vehicle piloting: ship 15
ENDURANCE 10
STRENGTH 10
TOUGHNESS 11
INTELLECT 9
Navigation: sea 14, perception 13, trick 12
MIND 8
Business 11
CONFIDENCE 11
Alteration: elemental 16, intimidation 16, willpower 15

Mike Vilardi

CHARISMA 9
Persuasion 14, taunt 14
Life Points: 5
Equipment: .38 Gelvash, damage value 17, ammo 6; blackjack, damage value STR+3/18
Arcane Knowledges: Water 1
Spells: *Ice dagger*

STANDARD SAILOR (HUMAN) (10)

Human sailors have all attributes at 8 save Agility, which is 9. They have melee combat and unarmed combat at 11, and are armed with clubs (damage value STR+5/20). Every sailor has one Life Point.

STANDARD SAILOR (ELKIST) (6)

AGILITY 8
Dodge 10, swimming 9, unarmed combat 10, unarmed parry 9
DEXTERITY 8
Fire combat 9, vehicle piloting: sailing vessel 11
ENDURANCE 9
STRENGTH 12
INTELLECT 8
First aid 9, navigation: sea 11
MIND 8
Cartography 9
CONFIDENCE 8

Gambling 10, intimidation 10, willpower 9
CHARISMA 8
Life Points: 1–3
Equipment: .38 Gelvash revolver, damage value 17, ammo 6; baton; duffel bag filled with clothing, assorted maps, and compass.

Roleplaying Notes: Elkists are crossbreeds between Ghouls and a demonic species that apparently no longer exists on Marl. An Elkist can cause any part of its body — hands, feet, arms, legs, head, neck and torso — to turn intangible, although it seems they do not have the ability to cause more than one part to do so at a time.

It is possible for an Elkist to trade up intangible parts. If the right arm is out of phase and the left arm about to be attacked, the Breed can bring the right limb back and phase out the left one simultaneously.

AFTERMATH

When the battle's over, the characters will be allowed to board the steamer. Read aloud or paraphrase:

The steamer is old, rusty and probably hasn't been cleaned in years. The berths you're given are cramped, especially since three of you have to share each one. As you're stowing

your gear, you see a pair of other passengers doing the same down the hall.

The other passengers are a man and a woman. The woman is extremely beautiful, with short red hair and a trim, athletic body covered with tattoos. The man is bundled up even more than the chill evening requires. Both somehow seem to rate their own berths.

The woman is Cat, owner of the Cat's Claw nightclub in Galitia. She's on her way to Dela to recruit some new fighters for the skinpits (she's a veteran of the fight circuit herself, which explains the body tattooing). She'll be polite to the characters, but not much more than that, and might be of some use in a fight later on.

CAT

AGILITY 12
Acrobatics 15, dodge 16, maneuver 16, stealth 16, unarmed combat 17, unarmed parry 17
DEXTERITY 8
Fire combat 10, thrown weapons 11
ENDURANCE 10
STRENGTH 9
TOUGHNESS 11
INTELLECT 9
First aid 11, perception 12, trick 13
MIND 9
Business 13, conjuration: technomancy 11
CONFIDENCE 9
Alteration: vitomancy 12, bribery 14, con 13, gambling 14, intimidation 13, streetwise 14, willpower 14
CHARISMA 11
Charm 16, persuasion 15, taunt 15
Life Points: 6
Alignment: Oathbreaker (Chaos) 1
Arcane Knowledges: Folk 2
Spells: *Dagger, slow*
Equipment: .22 Delken, damage value 15, ammo 6; throwing dagger, damage value STR+2/17
Roleplaying Notes: Cat is a veteran skinpit fighter who hasn't forgotten any of her moves in the years since she quit that racket. Today, though, she relies more on her powers of persuasion than her ability to break your arm in three places with one blow.

The male is not a Human at all, though he looks like one beneath the jacket, et. al. He is a Trexus, a large, bipedal lizard with great carnivorous jaws, and a 'Shifter to boot. This particular Trexus, named Kesk, is a Provider — it's his job to line up sacrifices to the dark gods of his people. Ambitious by nature, Kesk as decided to hijack this ship and divert it into a little cove between Galitia and Dela, then turn passengers and crew over to his people.

KESK

AGILITY 8/10
Climbing 10/12, stealth 10/12, unarmed combat 11/13
DEXTERITY 8/7
Thrown weapons 10/—
ENDURANCE 9/9
STRENGTH 9/11
TOUGHNESS 10/ 12 (10)
INTELLECT 8/7
First aid 9/8, perception 12/11, trick 11/10
MIND 9/9
Conjuration: necromancy 11/11
CONFIDENCE 8/6
Con 10/8, intimidation 9/10, willpower 11/9
CHARISMA 9
Charm 13, persuasion 13, shapeshifting 11
Life Points: 5
Attribute Notes: The numbers after the slash refer to reptilian form, while the prior number is for the creature's Human form.
Alignment: Chaos 4
Natural Tools: Hide, armor value TOU+2/12; teeth, damage value STR+3/14; claws, damage value STR+2/13
Spells: *Fires of death*
Arcane Knowledges: Fire 1

CUT TO...

Once the characters are ready to ship out, cut to Scene Two.

SCENE TWO: THE THING IN THE HOLD

THE SITUATION

Standard. The *Jolly Marie* begins its voyage, with passengers, crew and mysterious cargo. In this scene, the characters discover a little more about said cargo, and get their first look at the dread secret that lurks in the hold ... and maybe their last?

Read aloud or paraphrase:

Supper was about what you expected — old meat, decent ale, and a few crusts of bread. The crew kept to themselves, as did the top-coated passenger. Only Cat exchanged hellos with you and a little chat about events in Galitia.

As it gets near to midnight, you prepare to bed down. The captain has made it plain you'll be working to earn your passage, starting first thing in the morning.

THE ACTION

Just as the characters are getting ready to go to sleep, they hear a ragged scream coming from the direction of the bow. It's a man's voice, and he screams a second time before he's abruptly silenced.

If the characters go out on deck, they'll find the night watch in an uproar, the captain bellowing at all and sundry, Cat trying to make some sense of it all and the mysterious other passenger hanging back and observing. As the characters approach, they'll hear the captain interrogating Miggins, an obviously shaken crewman.

Miggins explains that he, Clark, Danvers and Stroud were down in the hold, guarding it like they'd been ordered to. Everything seemed normal — then all of a sudden, Stroud started disappearing. He never made a sound as he faded away, like he didn't even know it was happening. When Danvers tried to find him, he vanished too. Clark and Miggins made for the hold, but along the way Clark's legs vanished out from under him. He was the one who screamed, just before he disappeared. Miggins bolted out and locked the hold behind him.

Captain Largo looks grim. The crewmen look fearful. Wolf orders a watch put on the hold — from the outside, this time — no one gets in or out without his express orders. The door is to remain locked at all times. The characters don't need a roll to tell he knows more than he's revealing. And the crew isn't happy about this situation at all.

The characters have a chance now to do a little detective work. With the crew worried about their safety, they're a little more willing to talk, even to strangers. But the characters will have to be careful not to do their investigating in earshot of the captain, or he'll put them off the ship ... without bothering to make landfall first.

Use the standard sailor stats above for any of the crew the characters talk to. They can find out the following:

✝ Miggings knows no more than he's told, except that the marked boxes — the ones the captain had stowed in special — seemed awfully light. One thing was certain, they didn't have gold in them! Still, the crew was told to sneak them on board and guard them well.

✝ Anyone on watch can state that nothing got on board ship from the river.

✝ The ship made one, extremely brief, unscheduled stop at Gimm. Largo's stated excuse was that the engine needed repairing. But they weren't in port anywhere near long enough to get something fixed. Still, the engine was working better when they left.

✝ Though there have been deaths on board ship before, never anything like this.

EVENT

The characters, aided by Cat, may want to investigate some of the ship. You can use the information below to allow them to do that, but at some point during their tour, there should be another death. Throw this in if things start to drag. The victim will be one of the men on watch. Whatever's in the hold managed to make its way out.

How? Simple — there's a portion of the deck missing. Not carved out, not broken, not burnt — just gone. Wolf, of course, immediately orders it covered over with planks and nailed shut.

SEARCHING THE SHIP

Here are some quick notes on various portions of the ship:

The Mess: There's nothing of interest to be learned here. There is some good food, though, for the captain's personal use.

The Engine Room: Everything seems to be shipshape. Any character with some knowledge of engines can take a look at it and see it's running fine. A Mind, *science: engineering* or *vehicle mechanic: ship* total of 9 will reveal that some wires on the engine had apparently snapped and needed to be fused back together, which they were. An Intellect or perception total of 10 will reveal that they didn't just snap, though — they were cut. The engine was sabotaged, probably to force that stopover in Gimm.

Crew Cabins: Nothing of interest here, and the crew probably won't like having their privacy invaded.

Kesk's Cabin: Kesk will be cooperative. When the characters see him, he'll be in Human form to allay any fears they might have. Most of his belongings seem to be religious texts in some archaic language. If asked, he'll explain that he's a dealer in rare books, and is hoping to sell these to collectors in Dela. They date from before the first Godwar.

The Captain's Cabin: Characters had better be careful, because he's never gone for long. The door is locked (*lock picking* total of 10 to open). Inside are his personal belongings, a few crude maps of the river Skorn, and the ship's log. The log has a *lightning bolt* spell warded into it for any other hands but Wolf's, with three charges in it (damage value 21). Unless the characters have a way to a) destroy the spell or b) open the book without touching it, they'll have to take the three shots of the spell before they can read it. (If Cat is with them, she can explain that there are probably a limited number of charges in the book. Charges are expensive and one jolt to one crewman was probably enough to discourage all the others.)

Inside the log, the characters will see pretty much what they expect: details on the Galitia–Dela run, with two separate columns of figures. One relates to legitimate cargo and passengers, the other to contraband and smuggled criminals. Wolf has been doing a brisk business.

Brief mention is made of the stop in Gimm. There's reference to a cargo pick-up, and plans to sell whatever it was in Galitia. Later in the log, there's mention that the sale fell through and disposing of the cargo had proved to be a problem. Largo intends to stop at Gimm on his way back to Dela and make the seller take it back.

The Hold: Here's where things get interesting. The first problem the characters face is getting in there. There are two men on watch, and Wolf will have their hides if they let anyone in. The characters can bribe them, beat them, trick them, or use Cat to lure at least one of them away. Wolf hadn't bothered to ward the door, since too many people need to use it, plus he hadn't expected problems. The lock is iron and has a *lock picking* difficulty of 9.

Inside it's dark and smelly. Crates are stacked everywhere, including a number marked with the red serpent the characters might have seen on the dock. If they open one of these, using a convenient crowbar, they'll find lots of packing material and a few jars of a reddish powder. Any alchemists in the group, anyone with a knowledge of alchemy, anyone who has done any mining (and that lucky fellow who makes a Mind roll of 11) will recognize this as cinnabar, a valued and rare alchemical ingredient. It's not illegal to buy or sell it — it is, however, illegal to ship it without paying any duties. Everyone who thinks Largo paid duties on this stuff, stand on your head.

A *detect magic* rite will reveal traces of a *mystic chains* spell in the hold, which evidently didn't do its job. (If the characters weren't bright enough to post a watch, the hold doors slam shut and lock behind them at this point.) A spell to detect living beings will turn up *something* in the hold ... but it's not clear just what.

At least, not yet ...

SO WHAT IS IT?

Just what is in the hold? It's a gate ... worse, it's a *sentient* gate. There are certain creatures on Marl (at least, this is the theory), who exist both inside and outside of reality and are effectively walking gates. When they come in contact with a being from this plane, they absorb them into another one. That's what happened to the men in the hold.

This particular living gate was being transported from Gimm to Galitia by Largo when it broke free of the *mystic chains* spell (after all,

magic in this plane can only partially bind something that lives partway in another) and attacked its jailers.

SO LONG, IT'S BEEN GOOD TO KNOW YA

At this point, the gate attacks the first of the player characters. There are no rolls needed — gates of all sorts are gamemaster tools, to be used as they wish. One of the characters simply begins to fade away. He can attempt to run away, but the gate is as fast as you need it to be. Magic will slow the gate down, but not stop it — physical weapons have no effect on it.

The gate will grab as many people as it can, but it may be that some of the characters will escape to the deck. If they do, let them go — allowances are made in this adventure for this possibility, and you don't want to completely frustrate every escape attempt. As long as a few characters go through, you're fine.

CUT TO...

Once the gate has done its work, cut to Scene Three. Any characters left behind should cut to Scene Four.

SCENE THREE: WELCOME TO THE NEIGHBORHOOD

THE SITUATION

Standard. Read aloud or paraphrase:

One second you were in the hold ... the next, you're standing on a barren, twisted landscape. The sky above you is crimson; so is the blood pooling at your feet. Amidst a pile of clothes you recognize as belonging to one of the missing sailors, lie the torn remains of a Human infant.

You are on a plain, surrounded by low hills and rocky slopes. As you stand there, you hear a strange, chittering noise that steadily grows louder.

THE ACTION

The sound is coming from what can best be described as Demonlings, one of the denizens of this plane of existence. A half dozen are massing for

Mike Vilardi

an attack behind one of the hills. The characters have three rounds to hunt cover before the attack comes.

If the characters turn around to look for the gate, it's not there anymore.

STANDARD DEMONLINGS (10)

AGILITY 14
Climbing 16, long jumping 15, maneuver 15, stealth 15, unarmed combat 15
DEXTERITY 12
ENDURANCE 8
STRENGTH 11
TOUGHNESS 10
INTELLECT 8
Perception 9, tracking 9, trick 9
MIND 6
CONFIDENCE 7
Intimidation 11, willpower 9
CHARISMA 5
Taunt 8
Life Points: 1
Natural Tools: Claws, damage value STR+4/15; teeth, damage value STR+3/14
Description: Demonlings are extremely low-order Demons, with no arcane abilities, simply heightened strength and agility. They tend to hunt and kill in packs, swarming over their prey and rending him to bits. In this way, they can take out foes much more powerful than they are.

The characters may get a little bloodied but they should be able to beat off the attack. During the fight, call for *perception* totals — on a 10, one of the characters notices two sets of Human tracks leading off into the hills.

If the characters choose not to follow this trail, cut to "Exploring."

Intellect or *tracking* totals of 8 will allow the characters to follow the trail. After some hard traveling through uneven country, hounded by flying insects that bore up out of the ground and retreat there when swatted at, the characters come upon a campsite.

The two surviving sailors are sitting around a campfire, obviously having been in a fight. They are finshing their dinner, what was apparently some sort of small pig. As the characters approach, the bones of the pig rejoin, the flesh grows back on it and the animal scamperrs away.

If the characters don't announce their presence somehow, one of the sailors might take a shot at them out of surprise. But overall they will be glad to see semi-familiar faces in this strange place.

Their tale is not very different from that of the characters'. After they emerged from the gate to find themselves here, Stroud gave a yell. They turned to see him growing younger by the second.

By the time the Demonlings attacked, he wasn't much more than a kid. There was no way he could fight the things off.

This entire place is screwy. They killed the animal, saw it decompose before their eyes, return to normal, then spring back to life after they had eaten it. So far, they haven't seen anything that looks like a way out of this place.

EXPLORING

The characters will come upon some of these places as they go exploring this plane:

The River: The characters hear the sound of a rushing river and can smell the water. By the time they reach the site, it's a dry riverbed. They'll have to cross it to proceed. Simple, right? Except that time snaps back the other way when they're halfway through, and they're suddenly in the middle of a raging torrent. Agility or swimming rolls of 12 are going to be required to stay afloat. Failure means the character goes under, suffering damage value 16. If the character relaxes, goes limp, and lets the water carry him, he'll be fine — except for those rocks in the water, of course.

Once the characters are sufficiently wet and annoyed, the water vanishes again and they wind up flat on their backs in the dust.

Time Heals All Wounds: At some point, all wounds suffered by the characters heal themselves, leaving no scars.

When I'm Old and Gray: One of the sailors suddenly lets out a groan, doubles over, and ages about 100 years in as many seconds, then drops dead.

Lassiter, You Say?: A pair of lassiters, Marl's fiercer big cats, got drawn into this plane quite a while ago. They're not happy about it.

LASSITER (2)

AGILITY 14
Climbing 18, dodge 16, long jumping 16, maneuver 17, running 16, stealth 20, unarmed combat 19, unarmed parry 16
DEXTERITY 5
ENDURANCE 12
STRENGTH 14
TOUGHNESS 13 (12)
INTELLECT 9
Perception 12, tracking 15, trick 10
MIND 6
CONFIDENCE 8
Intimidation 14, willpower 14
CHARISMA 5
Life Points: 3
Natural Tools: Teeth, damage value STR+4/18; teeth, damage value STR+3/17 — both should

be treated as if they have the "Armor Defeating Attack" Special Ability (negates armor adds up to +10); hide, TOU+1/13.

Description: Lassiters are carnivorous cats, normally solitary hunters who won't balk at stalking and killing anything that comes into their territory, regardless of species or size. Lassiters have claws and teeth capable of tearing through armor with ease, even the enchanted kind.

THE CAVE

Finally, the characters come upon a cave. Inside, there's a natural rock pedestal upon which a scroll, lit by its own illumination. The characters may not want to go inside, but then again, this is the only sign of civilization they've seen in this place ... and the only one they're likely to see. Certainly, the surviving sailor will go in, and nothing very bad will be seen to happen to him.

If the characters insist on wandering around, throw some more Demonlings at them. Make the place hellish enough and they'll grasp at any straw ... even at an illuminated one.

CUT TO...

If there are characters back on the ship, cut to Scene Four. If there aren't, cut to Scene Five.

SCENE FOUR: HIJACKED!

THE SITUATION

Standard. This is a very brief scene, almost an interlude for any player characters left behind on the ship. If none have been, you need not run this scene and can go straight to Scene Five.

The disappearance of the player characters will have the sailors good and frightened. The remaining characters can use this to force answers out of Largo. This will require intimidation, threats of physical force, and the like, as Largo is a tough nut to crack.

Once Largo starts to talk, this is his story:

"Not much to tell. I heard through friend of a friend of a friend that there was this trapper in Gimm, see? Seems he'd caught himself something real special and he knew of a guy in Galitia with the scratch to buy it. But he needed a way to get it there ... and he knew the *Jolly Marie* was the fastest ship on these waters.

"So I made the pick-up. At first, I thought

Jaime Lombardo & Ron Hill

he was conning me — I didn't see no Wilderness creature, just a lot of nothing. But then he threw a rat toward his beastie and the rat vanished into thin air! Came out the other side, he said, someplace else. He didn't know if it could ever find its way back.

"I let the thing on board, and cursed by the day I did! I guess the spell couldn't hold it ... and it'll take us all inside it, take us all to that other place, if it gets the chance."

THE ACTION

Give the characters a few moments to digest this news and think about plans of action. Then there's a scream and the mate goes flying through the window of the wheelhouse. Then the ship suddenly lurches to starboard and begins heading at a dangerous speed toward the rocky shore!!

If the characters glance into the wheelhouse, they'll notice their topcoated friend at the wheel, sending the ship to a sure collision. If they glance toward shore, they'll see a crowd of Trexus forming ... all that's missing and knives and forks.

The characters can attack Kesk if they wish, and might even beat him. But not in time to keep the ship from slamming into the rocks ... (unless the characters make a successful Agility total of 14, they suffer a knockdown and two shock automatically from the collision).

CUT TO...

Once the ship has been wrecked, cut to Scene Five.

SCENE FIVE: IN THE BELLY OF THE BEAST

THE SITUATION

Dramatic. This scene assumes the characters have entered the cavern. Before them rests the scroll, just waiting to be read. If one of the characters picks it up, read aloud or paraphrase:

The scroll is undeniably ancient, and yet the ink on it is still wet, another manifestation of time's bizarre behavior in this place. It reads:

"Know that in this place, the gods of Chaos and Order did make war. So great was their struggle that the heavens shook, the oceans boiled, and all that was ceased to be. The

blood of the gods burned this planet to a cinder, and then recreated it as you see it now, travelers.

"Here there be beasts who live beyond death; powers far beyond mortal comprehension; here, you are born again — you have no past, only future.

"Here, time is both master and slave, bending and breaking all who come before it. Step softly, travelers, lest you be crushed beneath the weight of years.

"Of course, most of the above is a crock ... but it did keep you standing still just long enough for the 'cave' to know you're here."

THE ACTION

Just as these lines are read, jagged rows of stone slam shut on the cavern entrance ... jagged rows of stone that look uncomfortably like teeth. A low rumble travels through the ground that sounds almost like laughter.

Yes, the characters are inside a living creature. They're also now in pitch darkness if they didn't bring a light. Going back the way they came ain't an option — they'll have to go forward. Won't that be fun?

After about 20 meters, the tunnel begins to slope downward. This creature's "digestive tract" is interwoven with the planet itself. Unfortunately, it takes quite a while for this thing to digest its meals, meaning some of them are still alive in here ...

In point of fact, about a quarter of the way through the tunnel, the characters will stumble upon a nest of phexen. The phexen will not be happy about this. What do phexen do when they're unhappy? They carve you to pieces, that's what.

STANDARD PHEXEN (12)

AGILITY 12
Flight 14, maneuver 15, stealth 17, unarmed combat 16
DEXTERITY 4
ENDURANCE 9
STRENGTH 10
Lifting 11
TOUGHNESS 12 (9)
INTELLECT 4
Perception 15, tracking 10, trick 7
MIND 4
CONFIDENCE 5
Intimidation 8, willpower 11
CHARISMA 4
Life Points: None
Natural Tools: Bladed "hands" damage value STR+3/13; shell, armor value TOU+3/12; mandibles, damage value STR+2/12

Notes: Phexen should be considered to have the "Intangibility" Special Ability, and "Enhanced Senses" added to both vision and hearing.

Description: Phexen are an insectoid species, possibly with a little Undead mixed in there somewhere. The upper half of their bodies resembles a large insect's, with two long, spindly arms that end in sharp blades. There is no lower half of their body — instead it looks as if it were torn away in some past battle. The phexen's multifaceted eyes and sensitve antennae allow it to both spot prey and sense its motion when it is not in view.

The phexen commonly hovers aboveground, but when attacking or threatened, it will go intangible and sink beneath the earth. It will then pass through soil and rock and emerge again, either far from its foe or directly behind him, the better to take him unawares. Phexen seem to need to resurface every 50 meters or so, perhaps to breath.

Phexen fight using their arms, which can slice prey to pieces. Once a target it downed, they will consume it with their mandibles.

I HAVE A LITTLE SHADOW

Phexen aren't the characters' only worry as they travel through the winding, twisting stone tunnel. You see, they're also being stalked by shadowers (for a full description of these, see page 42 of *The World of Bloodshadows*. Stats are listed here for your convenience.)

STANDARD SHADOWER (3)

AGILITY 12
Dodge 14, long jumping 13, maneuver 13, stealth 23, unarmed combat 15
DEXTERITY 6
ENDURANCE 9
STRENGTH 11
TOUGHNESS 11
INTELLECT 12
Camouflage 17, perception 19, tracking 16, trick 15
MIND 8
CONFIDENCE 9
Intimidation 18 (invoking paranoia 20), survival: Wilderness 11
CHARISMA 12
Taunt 14
Life Points: 3
Natural Tools: Claws, damage value STR+3/14; "Invisiblity" as listed under "Special Abilities (CIV) Invisibility" in Chapter Five of The World of Bloodshadows.

Make sure the shadowers don't attack until after the phexen encounter. The insects should help lean the characters toward real paranoia.

Mike Vilardi

With any luck, they'll be shooting at each other before they get out of this tunnel!

THE WAY HOME

Eventually, the characters will emerge from the tunnel and back into the daylight (yes, they are emerging from an excretory passage ... try not to think about it). In fact, they are back on the plain upon which they first emerged.

Amazingly, some distance before them, they see a ripple in space. The next instant, a small group of figures steps out on to the rocky ground — it's themselves!

Let this event go on long enough for the characters to figure out what they're seeing. Time has shifted again here, returning that area to the moment when the characters first arrived. If they hurry, they can get back through the gate and wind up back on the Jolly Marie! If they don't ... well, who knows how long it will be before a gate shows up again, or where it might lead?

CUT TO...

Once the characters are back through the gate and once more in the hold of the ship, cut to Scene Six.

SCENE SIX: NO SACRIFICE IS TOO GREAT

THE SITUATION

Dramatic. Okay, here's the scene: the characters are back from the other plane and in the hold of the ship. Any characters left behind are probably up on deck. The ship has just crashed into the rocks, and there's a beach full of Trexus just waiting to sacrifice the characters, the crew, Largo and Cat to their gods. (Figured the gate would drop the characters off right about when they left, didn't you? Well, you were wrong ... things on that other plane are nowhere near that neat and orderly.

THE ACTION

Basically, this is a very straightforward action scene. The Trexus want to kill and feast on the characters and the crew. The characters should

want to prevent this. The ship is sinking, and the Trexus are perfectly content to wait until it sinks and pick the characters off one by one in the water. So the best strategy is to take the fight to them on the beach.

STANDARD TREXUS (15) (LIZARD FORM)
AGILITY 10
Climbing 12, stealth 12, unarmed combat 13
DEXTERITY 7
ENDURANCE 9
STRENGTH 11
TOUGHNESS 12 (10)
INTELLECT 7
Perception 12/11, trick 10
MIND 9
Conjuration: necromancy 11
CONFIDENCE 6
Intimidation 10, willpower 9
CHARISMA 9
Shapeshifting 11
Life Points: 2
Alignment: Chaos 4
Natural Tools: Hide, armor value TOU+2/12; teeth, damage value STR+3/14; claws, damage value STR+2/13

The characters emerging from the hold have the element of surprise on their side initially, as Kesk thinks them dead and hasn't bothered to warn his comrades of them.

If the battle proves a little too tough, the gate creature can begin absorbing some of the Trexus. At some point in the battle, especially if some characters are still on the ship, have the ship begin to disappear as the gate absorbs it.

AFTERMATH

Surviving is a victory here. The characters are left with no ship, stranded in the Wilderness somewhere between Galitia and Dela. Finding their way back to a city is an adventure unto itself. They and any of the other survivors had best get started — before that gate finds them again. (Cat might be willing to offer future employment to the characters, the next time they're in Galitia.)

AWARDS

Award all surviving characters two skill points apiece for successfully completing this adventure. Also award each one four Life Points.

CHAPTER NINE

DEATH BY DIME NOVEL

In this adventure, the characters are hired by dime novelist Gibson Walters, a kindly old sort who has suddenly found himself suspected as a mass murderer. Walters has been quarreling for years with his publishers, B. Lou Cole and Co., over royalties he feels are due him. Just recently, the publishers invoked a clause in his old contract and seized ownership of all the characters Walters created.

Soon after that, the deaths began. One by one, B. Lou Cole executives began to be murdered, each in a different way, but each in the style of one of Walters' characters. Naturally, sentinel suspicions were roused, but the author insists on his innocence.

As the characters investigate, they find that the contract stipulates that if Cole and Co. goes under, all rights revert back to the author — motive? They also run afoul of more than a few of Galitian pulp fiction's classic heroes and villains, as well as a few red herrings.

In the end, it's discovered that Walters did intend to send one of his characters to throw a scare into the publishers, but things went horribly wrong. The spell was too powerful, the characters, malevolent. (In fact, Walters' wife tampered with the ritual.) Now, it seems, they cannot be stopped …

SCENE ONE: PRINTER'S DEVIL

THE SITUATION

Standard. The characters can receive word of Gibson Walters' plight in any one of a number of ways. If this adventure is part of an ongoing campaign, the characters might notice reports in the newspapers of the deaths of B. Lou Cole executives. All have been killed in strange and unusual ways which might ring a vague bell with the characters, but probably won't immediately make sense. The characters might also learn of the ongoing situation from sentinel contacts, streetsingers, newscribe pals, or through other means (news travels fast in Galitia). The point is to let them have a little information prior to their being approached by Walters.

At some point, one of the characters will get a call from Walters' secretary, Deborah Robbins, inviting them to his home for a meeting on "very important business."

Assuming the characters accept, they'll travel to the Canons district of Galitia and a modest, unassuming home tucked away on a sidestreet. Robbins will greet them at the door.

THE ACTION

Read aloud or paraphrase:

The door is opened by an exquisitely beautiful young woman, petite with brown hair and a brilliant smile. Still, behind the warm greeting, you can see traces of worry.

"It's good of you to come on such short notice," she says. "The sentinels have been no help at all and Mr. Lane can only advise us to sit and wait. But the tension is killing Mr. Walters. Someone has to do something."

If asked, Robbins reveals that Mr. Lane is Walters' advocate. However, she won't reveal anything more about the reason the characters were summoned, preferring to leave that to her employer. She will usher the characters into the study. Read aloud:

The room is a shrine of sorts to decades of pulp fiction. On the walls are framed covers from some of Gibson Walters' dime novels: "The Wraith and the Golden Master," "The Wraith Challenged," "Coils of the Queskworm," "Terror From the Deep," "The Wraith vs. Curses Inc.," the list goes on and on. The bookshelves are filled with hundreds of copies of Wraith novels and the The Wraith Mystery Magazine. On a desk in the corner sits a battered old typewriter and some scribepads.

From behind them, a friendly voice says, "This is all I have left. Now I may lose even this."

Walters is an older man, in his early 60s, with white hair, glasses, and a round face. He wears a dark suit and shakes the hand of each and every character before inviting them to sit down.

His story is a straightforward one and contains the following facts:

† He's been writing for the dime novels and magazines since he was 17. He created his most famous character, the Wraith, "He Who Walks With the Spirits," when he was 23, and went on to write over 700 novels featuring the character.

† His publishers, B. Lou Cole and Co., have been withholding his royalty payments for almost 10 years now, despite all his efforts to get what he's owed. Most recently, they invoked a clause in the contract that gave them the rights to the Wraith and all the other characters Walters had created. His advocates have told him it's all perfectly legal,

and as perfect a swindle as they've ever seen.

† The nightmare began shortly after he got the news. John Woodruff, Cole and Co.'s attorney, was found strangled with a golden chain and turned to gold — bizarre, but not suggestive of anything, except to fans of the Wraith. One of his earliest villains was an assassin named Aureus, who specialized in slaying his victims with golden weapons. A few days later, one of the firm's accountants was pulverized in a manner similar to that employed by Bonecrusher, another of the Wraith's foes. Finally, the senior editor was literally frightened to death … the favorite killing method of Baron Fear, one of the Wraith's most dangerous opponents. But all of these are fictional creations.

Naturally, the sentinels are assuming that Walters — or one of his fans — is copying the methods of his creations to slay the men who swindled him. They have no hard evidence yet, but Cole is putting pressure on them to arrest the author.

Walters wants to avoid arrest, naturally, but he's also sick with guilt that his creations are being used to murder. He wants the real killer or killers stopped before his reputation — and that of the Wraith — are ruined forever.

GIBSON WALTERS

AGILITY 7
DEXTERITY 7
ENDURANCE 8
STRENGTH 8
TOUGHNESS 9
INTELLECT 10
Deduction 14, perception 14, trick 13
MIND 11
Artist: writer 17, conjuration: vitomancy 17, research 15, scholar: pulp fiction 15
CONFIDENCE 9
Willpower 12
CHARISMA 10
Charm 14, persuasion 14
Life Points: 3
Arcane Knowledges: Life 4, folk 4
Roleplaying Notes: Despite his anxiety, Walters is still basically a charming man. He is confused and troubled by guilt (since he is ultimately responsible for his characters' being on the loose), but that will probably come off just as natural regret over these tragedies.

As is obvious, Walters was at one time a very accomplished vitomancer. He has since let those skills erode somewhat and has forgotten those spells he knew in his youth (his parents had wanted him to become a healer). Nowadays he is largely dependent on grimoires and other pre-packaged spells, which made him vulnerable to having the spell that conjured up the Wraith and the others tampered with.

HE WHO WALKS WITH THE SPIRITS

"Once the Wraith was a man like other men … Dan Thompson, gambler, afflicted with all the vices Humans are heir to. Until the day he was gunned down in an alley by mobsters, and ascended only to find that the Wraiths of the innocents slain there had interceded on his behalf. A power from beyond returned Thompson to Marl and gave him the power to walk both the mortal and the spirit planes. Aided by the spectres that haunt this world, Thompson stalks crime as that dread avenger, He Who Walks With the Spirits … The Wraith."

— From *The Wraith Strikes,* by Gibson Walters

"Ray Murphy was a small-time technomancer with big-time dreams. Obsessed with finding a way to create real gold and make it a permanent effect, he tampered with 'wild magic.' The spell backfired, sending a surge of energy through his body, transforming him, bestowing on him the power to turn anything — or anyone — to gold for one hour. Driven mad by the experience, Murphy vowed to slay anyone else who dared to possess gold. He trained himself in the ways of combat and became Galitia's deadliest assassin: Aureus, the Golden Reaper. In many ways, he is the Wraith's deadliest foe, due to that hero's vulnerability to gold and the fact that Aureus is the only man who knows the true identity of the man behind the mask of the Wraith."

— From *The Golden Doom,* by Gibson Walters

"Some say he's a Hugor gone bad. Some say he's an alchemical experiment left to boil too long. Others, that he's a remnant from a bygone age when giants walked Marl. The only thing anyone's sure about is that Bonecrusher lives up to his name. Usually the pawn of other criminals, Bonecrusher got his start as a legbreaker for flesh mill owners, then became a skullbreaker for the local mobs. More than once, he's clashed with the Wraith and lost and he remains driven by a lust for revenge."

— From … *But Bonecrusher Can Kill You,* by Gibson Walters

"'When an alchemist goes bad, he's the worst of criminals,' goes the old saying. Alexander Mills is the proof of that. Once an employee of a major alchemical firm in Galitia, Mills' twisted mind turned to the study of fear. He developed his *fear* potion and became convinced that he could rule the city using this new weapon. Donning the distinctive costume and skull-faced mask of Baron Fear, he launched a reign of terror until he was stopped by the Wraith. Long believed dead, he has in truth been nursing his wounds and planning for his next encounter with He Who Walks With the Spirits."

— From *Seven Nights of Baron Fear,* by Gibson Walters

After he is done explaining the situation, Mrs. Walters makes an appearance. She's an elderly woman trying desperately to look young. She makes no secret of her disapproving of the hiring of the characters, but in the end, seems willing to condescend to Gibson's whims. She makes no secret of her dislike for Cole and Co., but also expresses confidence that her husband can create something just as popular and successful as the Wraith and put the publisher to shame.

VERONICA WALTERS

AGILITY 8
Dodge 9, stealth 9
DEXTERITY 8
ENDURANCE 7
STRENGTH 7
TOUGHNESS 9
INTELLECT 10
Perception 12, trick 14
MIND 9
Business 11
CONFIDENCE 10
Alteration: vitomancy 11, con 13, intimidation 13, willpower 14
CHARISMA 8
Charm 10, persuasion 11, taunt 10
Life Points: 2
Arcane Knowledges: Living forces 1
Spells: *Facade*
Roleplaying Notes: Veronica Walters has a head for business. First, she saw her husband being swindled by his publishers and then she did a little reading and discovered that if Cole and Co. went out of business, Gibson would get all rights back. Before she could do anything about it on her own, she discovered that Gibson was planning a stunt of his own, sending the magically made real Wraith to frighten Cole executives. That suggested another plot to her: eliminating the Cole company *and* framing her husband for the deaths, so all the rights would go to her.

The characters can obtain addresses of the dead men from Walters. Cole has rejected the idea of sentinel protection, because he doesn't want the bad publicity for the firm.

Robbins comes in at this point to remind Walters that he and his wife have a lunch appointment. Have the characters generate Intellect or *perception* totals — on a 9, they'll notice the dirty look Mrs. Walters is directing toward Robbins. As the author's wife turns to leave, she bumps a table and a thin gold bracelet falls from her wrist to the floor. Robbins bends to pick it up and return it — Mrs. Walters snatches it back.

Once the Walters are gone, the characters can question Robbins further. She'll admit that she has heard Gibson Walters in violent conversation with Cole and other executives of the publisher — even to the point of threatening his life, once. But she's certain he's not capable of murder, or even of hiring someone to commit murder. And even if he were … why use methods certain to point straight to him?

As for Mrs. Walters' jealousy, it's completely unfounded. Mr. Walters is old enough to be Robbins' father and is no more than her employer. But she admits that her loyalty to him may be stronger than that of his wife — that gold bracelet, for instance, was never given to her by her husband, of that she's sure.

DEBORAH ROBBINS

AGILITY 9
Stealth 10, unarmed combat 10
DEXTERITY 8
ENDURANCE 8
STRENGTH 8
TOUGHNESS 9
INTELLECT 10
Deduction 12, first aid 11, perception 13, trick 12
MIND 9
Business 13, scholar: pulp fiction 12
CONFIDENCE 10
Alteration: vitomancy 12, willpower 14
CHARISMA 13
Charm 18, persuasion 16
Life Points: 3
Arcane Knowledges: Living forces 2
Spells: *Awaken, first aid*
Roleplaying Notes: Deborah is an incredibly beautiful and charming woman. She is also an able assistant to Gibson Walters, keeping track of his deadlines and commitments and even assisting him when his plots run into a brick wall. She has long been an object of Veronica Walters' hostility, something she has learned to accept.

CUT TO...

There are a couple of obvious directions for the characters to go at this point, including examining the murder scenes, talking to the sentinels, and researching some of Walters' writings. Move on to Scene Two.

SCENE TWO: THE GOLDEN TOUCH

THE SITUATION

Standard. The characters begin investigating the murders, with their leads taking them toward another of Cole and Co.'s financial officers, George Crane, who reveals a possible motive for the murders of the executives. Then he finds himself the next target of Aureus, the Golden Reaper.

Below you'll find some of the courses of action the characters might choose to take and the results of them. Inevitably, the characters will be brought face to face with George Crane.

THE ACTION

The characters may choose to do the following:
Talk to the Sentinels: If the characters have contacts among the sentinels, they can talk with them about the murders and get some information (this also works if the characters know streetsingers or newscribes, who can provide much of the same information). The sentinels strongly suspect Walters of involvement in the killings, with a motive of revenge. They're hoping to get their hands on one of the killers and force him to name Walters as the man behind the crimes. In the meantime, they're providing protection for other Cole and Co. executives.

Examine the Crime Scenes: This might be tricky, as the sentinels aren't likely to just let anyone tramp through a murder scene. But just by being around, the characters will hear a telling fact muttered by the sentinels: there seems to be no sign of any forced entry or exit, and all the doors and windows were locked. That means the killer or killers might have access to dimensional magic and be popping in and out, which will make it much more difficult to make an arrest.

Reading Walters' Writings: The characters can find Wraith novels at dime stores, streetsinger stands, maybe even in a library (though the latter

is more doubtful). There they can find the origins of Walters' characters (see sidebar).

WHERE'S GEORGE?

Any attempts to speak with B. Lou Cole executives will meet with failure. They're under orders not to speak with anyone except the sentinels about the goings-on (and sometimes not even them). But once the characters have exhausted all other avenues and returned to their favorite nightspot or their apartments, one will get a phone call. The speaker on the other end will ask if they are investigating the Cole Co. murders. If they admit that they are, he'll give them an address in the Vrenthar district and a time, 10 p.m. He'll promise them information that will point to the man behind the killings.

At the appointed time and the appointed place, the characters will find themselves before a respectably large house, though by no means a mansion. The owner is a substantial gentleman named George Crane, junior partner in the publishing firm. At first glance, he doesn't seem like the type who rattles easily — but rattled he is, and badly.

GEORGE CRANE

AGILITY 7
Dodge 8, maneuver 8, unarmed combat 8
DEXTERITY 7
ENDURANCE 8
STRENGTH 8
TOUGHNESS 9
INTELLECT 9
Cantrips 10, deduction 12, linguistics 11, perception 12
MIND 10
Business 13
CONFIDENCE 10
Willpower 12
CHARISMA 9
Charm 11
Life Points: 2
Spells: *Note*
Roleplaying Notes: Crane is a younger man with an enthusiasm for his work and his life. Wherever he goes, he walks briskly as if he has something crucial he has to do there.

Crane has seen three business associates die in a frighteningly short amount of time, and is convinced he'll be next. If asked who he thinks is responsible for the murders, he doesn't waste a second in naming Gibson Walters, and he insists he has proof. What is it? He whips out a copy of Walters' contract with Cole and Co. and points to the fine print — the clause that reads "should the firm ever purchase or otherwise obtain the rights to

the fictional characters, rights will revert to the author only upon the firm's dissolution." In other words, if the publisher goes under, Walters would own the Wraith again. The clause goes on to state that should the author retain the rights to the characters, they would pass on to his next of kin upon his death.

Looks like a pretty damning bit of evidence, doesn't it? Evidently, the killer thinks so, too — just as Crane leans over to show them some fine print, the window is shattered. Crane stiffens, slumps, and falls over dead, a golden knife in his back.

Aureus has arrived. And Aureus hates leaving witnesses.

AUREUS

AGILITY 11
Dodge 15, maneuver 16, melee combat 15, melee parry 15, unarmed combat 16
DEXTERITY 13
Fire combat 16, missile weapons: crossbow 16, thrown weapons 17
ENDURANCE 11
STRENGTH 11
TOUGHNESS 11
INTELLECT 10
Demolitions 12, perception 14, science: weaponsmith 14, smuggling 13, tracking 15, trick 14
MIND 8
CONFIDENCE 9
Conjuration: alchemy 13, conjuration: technomancy 14, intimidation 15, willpower 14
CHARISMA 9
Taunt 11
Life Points: 6
Arcane Knowledges: Metal 2
Spells: *Dagger*
Equipment: Aureus is a master of many weapons, all made of gold. On this job, he's carrying a crossbow, damage value STR+9/24; throwing daggers, damage value STR+2/17; knife, damage value STR+4/19; .38 Gelvash, damage value 17, ammo 6

Roleplaying Notes: As a result of the spell which conjured him, Aureus has the following special abilities: Attack Form Resistance (Magical Attacks); Paralyzing Touch (this works by turning the target to gold, but in all other ways is similar to the Background Advantage detailed on page 75 of *The World of Bloodshadows*).

Aureus has come for three reasons: to kill Crane, to kill anyone who's talked to Crane, and to retrieve that copy of the contract. He's managed one of his objectives, now it's up to the player characters to prevent him from achieving the other two.

Keep in mind that Aureus is a fictional character come to life, and will take daring chances and insane risks because he's used to being able to get away with them in the stories. He'll try to take the characters out long distance with his various thrown weapons, but won't shy away from physical combat, especially with his "golden touch."

If he's losing the combat badly, he'll try one last stratagem — turning any one of the characters to gold, and then setting the house on fire. The characters will have a choice: abandon their comrade, forget about chasing Aureus, or split up (remember that gold is extremely heavy, so carrying a full-grown adult now made out of that metal is going to take more than one pair of hands).

Naturally, Aureus doesn't really need to make an escape — he can blink out of existence at will, thanks to the nature of the spell. But he is so used to having to elude pursuit in his fictional life that he is doing it from force of habit.

AFTERMATH

Whether or not Aureus is defeated is not crucial to this scene. What is crucial is that the characters somehow get B. Lou Cole's home address, because he is the next target. This can be from Crane's dying words, a note found in his desk (assuming it's not destroyed in the fire), etc. It doesn't matter, as long as they get the clue.

CUT TO...

There's very little time to lose. The characters need to get to Cole's address before another of Walters' characters makes it there.

SCENE THREE: ...BUT BONECRUSHER CAN KILL YOU

THE SITUATION

Standard. The characters arrive at Cole's house just a little too late, or so it seems. Read aloud or paraphrase:

Getting into Cole's manor house in Vrenthar evidently won't be the problem you had expected. The two guards at the gate have been pulped, and the gate itself has seen its bars torn apart. Bonecrusher might as well have signed his name ...

And he's not exactly being subtle, either. Long before the characters make it across the lawn and to the house, they'll hear the sounds of furniture being smashed within. Bonecrusher is thoroughly enjoying his new existence.

THE ACTION

This is a flat-out action scene. Bonecrusher is busily trashing Cole's mansion, having apparently forgotten completely his reason for being there: kidnapping the publisher. The characters can choose their means of entry — the broken windows, the smashed front door, etc. — and challenge him. He's a largely inarticulate brute, but good at what he does: hurting people.

BONECRUSHER

AGILITY 9
Unarmed combat 13, unarmed parry 13
DEXTERITY 7
ENDURANCE 15
Resist shock 16
STRENGTH 15
Lifting 17
TOUGHNESS 13
INTELLECT 6
Perception 8
MIND 5
CONFIDENCE 8
Intimidation 16, willpower 14
CHARISMA 7
Life Points: 3

Roleplaying Notes: Bonecrusher is a massive, bald man loaded with muscles. He needs no weapons other than his bare fists and sheer strength. The spell that summoned him also gifted him, on this plane, with Attack Form Resistance (Non-Enchanted Weapons).

Have fun with this battle. Let it spill through various rooms of the house, with all sorts of priceless works of art and antique furniture being wrecked in the process. Remember that, although Bonecrusher isn't smart enough to consciously use his ability to pop into and out of existence, when his mind wanders he does it anyway. This means you can have him appearing and disappearing at will, just to keep it from being too easy for the player characters.

Eventually, he will make a stand and the characters should defeat him. An Intellect or *perception* total of 9 reveals a slip of paper tucked into his belt. Written on it is an address in the warehouse district of Esler. Could this be the hideout of the murderous characters come to life?

A search of the house to find Cole will turn up no sign of the publisher. However, *perception* totals of 9 in his study will uncover splashes of a strange, reddish liquid with a sickly sweet smell. The characters can take some to get tested by an alchemist, or they may remember it from reading Walters' stories — it's Baron Fear's potion of terror. The Baron has been here and gone while Bonecrusher acted as a diversion!

CUT TO...

Oops. Guess the characters shouldn't have spent so much time on Bonecrusher, hmmmm? Now Cole is gone and they're left with an engraved invitation to a hideaway … or a trap? Cut to Scene Four, "Fear is the Key."

SCENE FOUR: FEAR IS THE KEY

THE SITUATION

Standard. The characters make their way to the hideout of Baron Fear, only to discover that the warehouse is indeed a trap … and they're about to come face to face with their deadliest enemies.

Read aloud or paraphrase:

It certainly looks like a hideout out of the pulps. An old, abandoned warehouse surrounded by other empty buildings and a rabbit warren of dark alleys. The only figures on the street, trying hard to look casual, are a few stony-faced types and some ridiculously thin gunmen.

THE ACTION

The warehouse is guarded by four Grani and four skeletal thugs (conjured up using the *thug from beyond* spell in *Sorcerers' Cribsheet*). There are two entrances to the warehouse, an employee door on the front and a loading bay around the side. The characters are going to have to get past the guards to get inside, and too much noise is sure to tip off those already inside.

GRANI (4)
AGILITY 6
Dodge 8, melee combat 10, melee parry 8, unarmed combat 9
DEXTERITY 8
ENDURANCE 12
Resist shock 13
STRENGTH 12
Lifting 14
TOUGHNESS 18 (13)
INTELLECT 9
Demolitions 11, perception 11
MIND 8
CONFIDENCE 8
Intimidation 10, streetwise 9, willpower 9
CHARISMA 7
Shapeshifting 9
Life Points: 1

Natural Tools: Stone flesh, armor value TOU+5/18

Roleplaying Notes: Grani are men made of a strange, stone-like material who are capable of changing the shape of their body or a portion of it. They have the natural ability to sense the "health" of the ground on which they're standing. The Grani are most likely to fight by shaping their hands into sledgehammers, picks, and other implements of destruction and smacking the characters with them. Grani are incapable of regenerating lost pieces of themselves, so anything that gets broken stays broken.

SKELETAL THUG (4)
AGILITY 12
Dodge 14, maneuver 14, unarmed combat 14
DEXTERITY 11
Fire combat 13
STRENGTH 13
ENDURANCE 13
TOUGHNESS 12
INTELLECT 11
Perception 13, tracking 12, trick 12
MIND 10
CONFIDENCE 10
Intimidation 14, willpower 12
CHARISMA 9
Taunt 10
Life Points: None
Natural Weaponry: Claws, damage value STR+3/16
Equipment: Skandra "Annihilator," damage value 17, ammo 30

Roleplaying Notes: These skeletal thugs are single-minded types. Normally, they are sent to do rub-outs and they're probably chafing a little at guard duty. If they so much as get a glimpse of a target, they'll open up with their Skandras, regardless of who's in the way.

ONLY THING WE HAVE TO FEAR

Once the guards are disposed of or lured away, the characters can enter the warehouse. It's pitch black inside, and there's no sound or sign of anyone. If the characters have a glowstone, they'll be able to see their surroundings — pretty much what you'd expect, crates with the names of alchemical components. An Intellect or *perception* total of 11 will reveal that there are glass decanters perched on a few of the crates, filled with some sort of liquid. The characters will have to move toward the center of the warehouse to get a good look at one … and when they do, they might notice a familiar reddish liquid.

At that instant, a mocking laughter will fill the warehouse and the bottles will explode, filling the warehouse with fumes (of course, holding one's breath

is an option — too bad the fumes slip through the pores of your skin. Undead characters, whose bodily systems work vastly different from those who are truly alive, are immune to the effects of these fumes.) This is, of course, Baron Fear's *fear* potion. It attacks the characters' minds with an *intimidation* value of 30 — characters will have to generate a Mind or *willpower* total to resist. Find the result points of the attack on the "Intimidation" column of the Success Chart (*MasterBook,* page 67) and determine the effects of the attack that way. If the result is a "player's call," the character so affected is mortally afraid of his comrades. Why, he might even shoot at them ... The effects of the attack last for ten minutes.

While the characters are wrestling with their fear, any guards left intact will show up and beat the stuffing out of them. All the while, Baron Fear will stand on the catwalk and gloat. Read aloud or paraphrase:

"Pitiful. Truly pitiful," the Baron exults. "Did you truly believe you had tracked me to my hideout? Tell me, of what use is a hideout to one who can do this?" Suddenly, the Baron vanishes, only to reappear a moment later. "I have all of non-existence to hide in.

"No doubt you are wondering just what I and my colleagues are planning. Why, the murder of Mr. Cole, of course, and the framing of Gibson Walters for the crime. Mrs. Walters has promised rewards for us in future tales — perhaps even series of our own — but I do not think I will be content with that. No, I like it here ... perhaps I will stay for a while, hmmmm? Not that any of you will be alive to see it, of course."

BARON FEAR

AGILITY 8
Climbing 9, dodge 10, stealth 10, unarmed combat 9
DEXTERITY 9
Thrown weapons 14
ENDURANCE 8
STRENGTH 8
TOUGHNESS 8
INTELLECT 12
Deduction 14, perception 15, science: chemistry 17, trick 15
MIND 12
Medicine 14, scholar: psychology 15
CONFIDENCE 11
Intimidation 18, willpower 16
CHARISMA 10
Charm 11, persuasion 14, taunt 16
Life Points: 4
Equipment: *Fear* potion (6), *intimidation* value of 30

Roleplaying Notes: In his costume designed to inspire terror, and armed with his trademark *fear* potions, Baron Fear is a formidable foe. The ritual that brought him here gifted him with Attack Form Resistance (Interaction).

With that, Baron Fear will make his escape (if at all possible) while the characters wrestle to overcome their fear (and the guards). Feel free to allow the characters periodic *willpower* totals to overcome the effects of the potion (if they manage to stumble out of the warehouse, add +5 to their *willpower* totals as the fresh air helps clear their heads).

The characters now know that framing Walters is part of the plot. That should suggest to them that his house might be the next logical place to go.

CUT TO...

When the characters are ready to head to Walters' house, cut to "Interlude," and then to Scene Five, "Shadow of the Wraith."

INTERLUDE

Well, here's an interesting development. The ruckus kicked up by Bonecrusher attacted the attention of B. Lou Cole's neighbors. And what did they see when they looked out their windows or peered through Cole's fence? Why, the characters fleeing the house, that's what. Couple that with the discovery that Cole was kidnapped and suddenly the party are the prime suspects.

Now they're racing the clock to get to Walters' house — the perfect time to sick some sentinels on them, ready to haul them in for questioning about the kidnapping.

STANDARD SENTINEL

AGILITY 9
Dodge 12, maneuver 10, melee combat 14, stealth 10, unarmed combat 13
DEXTERITY 9
Fire combat 13, vehicle piloting: wheeled 10
ENDURANCE 9
STRENGTH 9
TOUGHNESS 9
INTELLECT 8
Perception 12, tracking 9, trick 9
MIND 8
CONFIDENCE 8
Intimidation 9, streetwise 14, willpower 10
CHARISMA 8
Persuasion 9
Life Points: 4
Equipment: .38 Gelvash, damage value 17,

Jaime Lombardo & Ron Hill

ammo 6; hand-held crystal set; baton, damage value STR+3/18, *pain* spell; bullet-proof vest, armor value TOU+6/22

SCENE FIVE: SHADOW OF THE WRAITH

THE SITUATION

Dramatic. The characters arrive at Gibson Walters' house, sentinels quite possibly hot on their heels. They discover that the Wraith himself has made an appearance, and is holding B. Lou Cole captive, along with the Walters. Even if the characters succeed in turning the Wraith to their side, they will still have to face down his greatest enemies.

Read aloud or paraphrase:

The house of Gibson Walters is strangely silent, but volumes are spoken by the fact that the door is slightly ajar. In the distance, you can hear sirens wailing — the sentinels are closing in on you. Or are they coming for Walters? In the end, it doesn't really make very much difference, not if you can't stop Cole's murder.

THE ACTION

If the characters have any doubt about who is waiting for them in the house, they are dispelled as they begin to cross the lawn. No amount of stealth will be sufficient to evade the attention of the spirits commanded by the Wraith. As they approach the house, three Wraiths will rise up from the lawn and attempt to bar their way.

STANDARD WRAITH (3)

AGILITY 7
Dodge 9, unarmed combat 8, unarmed parry 8
DEXTERITY 8
Presitidigitation 11
ENDURANCE 6
STRENGTH 7
TOUGHNESS 9 (29 w/intangibility)
INTELLECT 12
Cantrips 13, divination: necromancy 15, perception 13, trick 13
MIND 13
Scholar: the Undead 15
CONFIDENCE 10
Alteration: chronomancy 13, willpower 12
CHARISMA 10
Life Points: 3
Natural Tools: Intangibility (through Trans-

mutation), armor value TOU+20/29; paralyzing touch, effect value CON+15/25

Arcane Knowledges: Death 1, Time 1
Spells: *Speak to dead, temporal fires*
Cantrips: *Candle, chill, heat, note*
Description: Wraiths are spectres of the dead, bound to remain within 10 kilometers of the site of their deaths. They are naturally intangible though, through an act of will, they can become tangible for short periods of time (up to one minute). For this reason, magic tends to be more effective against them than physical attacks, although they can be damaged with items that they possessed while still among the living.

Binding a Wraith in a circle of iron filings will disrupt its essence and effectively neutralize its powers for about a week, as well as causing it great pain. All *wounds* caused by items from their former lives are *doubled*.

These particular Wraiths serve the Wraith and are following his will in attempting to prevent the characters from reaching the house. One thing that may work on them (and the Wraith as well; see below) is pointing out that what the Wraith is about to do is unjust and wrong. If the characters achieve success on a *persuasion* roll — *and* do a good job of roleplaying — the Wraiths may let them pass.

THE WRAITH CHALLENGED

Inside the house, the characters will find the Wraith himself, holding twin .44s on B. Lou Cole, Gibson Walters and Deborah Robbins, while being egged on by Veronica Walters. She is speaking as the characters approach:

"Ironic, isn't it, Gibson? Destroyed by your own creation? In much the same way our marriage was destroyed, with you spending all your time pounding out those dreadful little books and cavorting with this ... this tart! Oh, yes, I knew she had designs on you from the very start, but I wasn't going to step aside, oh no! I earned the right to your fortune, and now I'm going to have it! When Cole dies his company dies with him — the rights to the Wraith become yours again, Gibson. And when you're sent to jail — or an asylum — they'll be mine. I'm sure the Wraith can find himself another publisher somewhere ... and another writer."

At this point, Gibson cuts her off, directing an impassioned plea to the Wraith. Read aloud or paraphrase:

"Listen to me! If there is anything in you of the character — the man — I created, you must not do this thing! The Wraith was in- tended to strike for justice, not evil. He was meant to be a symbol of what one man can accomplish. If you murder in cold blood ... you're no better than Aureus or Bonecrusher or any of the others you've fought over the years.

Or if you have to shoot someone, Wraith ... shoot me. I'm the one who conjured you up, you and the others. The fact that Veronica changed the ritual doesn't matter. I tried to use you for my own ends, something I had no right to do. If there is a crime here, Wraith, I'm the guilty one."

Even though he is masked, the Wraith's body language conveys a moment's doubt, a moment's hesitation. This is the crucial moment for the characters — they can reveal themselves and add their voices to Gibson Walters' plea, or they can attack.

If they do the former and are successful, the Wraith will relent. When the final battle comes, he will fight alongside the characters. If they fail, or they attack, he will have to be defeated to be stopped.

Regardless of what tack they take, Aureus, Bonecrusher and Baron Fear will make an appearance. Aureus will focus his attentions on Deborah Robbins, intending to turn her to gold and carry her off as a prize at the end of the battle. Bonecrusher will attack the characters. Baron Fear will attempt to frighten Cole to death.

THE WRAITH

AGILITY 12
Acrobatics 15, climbing 14, dodge 16, maneuver 15, melee combat 15, stealth 17, unarmed combat 16, unarmed parry 15
DEXTERITY 12
Fire combat 17
ENDURANCE 10
STRENGTH 10
TOUGHNESS 11
INTELLECT 10
Deduction 15, first aid 13, perception 14, tracking 14, trick 15
MIND 10
Conjuration: photomancy 14, research 13
CONFIDENCE 11
Con 18, interrogation 16, intimidation 16, streetwise 14, willpower 18
CHARISMA 11
Charm 14, disguise 15, persuasion 15, taunt 14
Life Points: 6
Arcane Knowledges: Darkness 2
Spells: *Dark cloud*
Roleplaying Notes: Garbed all in black and armed with twin .44s, the Wraith is the scourge of

the underworld in Gibson Walters' novels. Like true Wraiths, the Wraith can turn his body to mist form, as per intangibility, but there is no time limit on the ability. He can turn tangible at will but it takes one round to achieve this. When he does become intangible, his equipment does so as well.

The Wraith also has the ability to command the shades of the innocent who have died on a site. They will combat alongside him against injustice.

The Wraith has an Achilles Heel — Vulnerability (CIII) to objects made of gold.

AFTERMATH

If the characters persuaded the Wraith to help them, he will turn to them after the villains are defeated and say simply,

"This is not my world. I don't belong here. But there is still a way to make amends for the evil we brought to you and yours, Gibson Walters ..."

With the, the Wraiths reappear and snatch up Veronica Walters. As the Wraith fades back into his fictional universe, Veronica Walters goes with him, now lost forever to the "real world."

Gibson Walters will turn himself in to the sentinels but will get off with a light prison sentence. Cole, badly frightened, will be more inclined to negotiate with Walters for future stories and the return of his rights. And if one of the male characters has a Romance subplot in play, he might just get a date with Deborah Robbins ...

AWARDS

Award the characters two skill points apiece for successfully completing this adventure. Each character can also be awarded three Life Points.

INDEX TO THE WORLD OF BLOODSHADOWS/ UNNATURALS

Note: Page numbers without prefixes refer to pages in *The World of Bloodshadows*. Numbers preceded by UN refer to pages in *Unnaturals*.

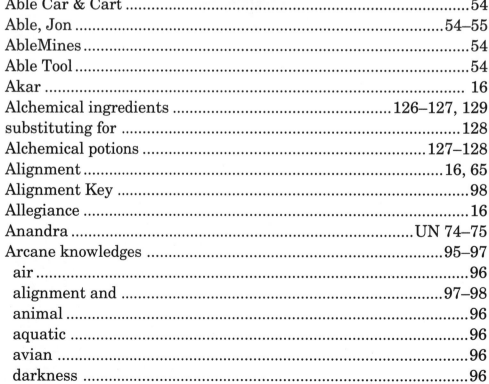

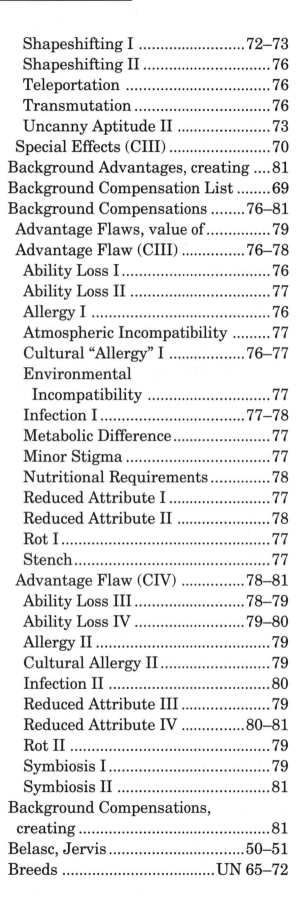

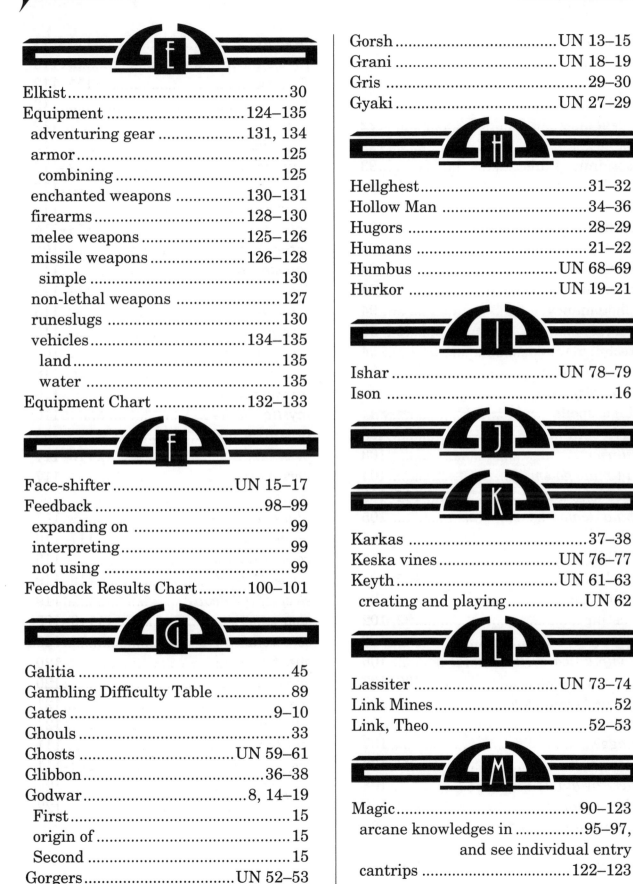

DIME NOVELIST

CHARACTER SHEET

SPECIES Human	**ALIGNMENT** Neutral	**HEIGHT**	**MASS**	**AGE**	**SEX** Male

ATTRIBUTES

AGILITY 7
Dodge 9
DEXTERITY 9
ENDURANCE 8
STRENGTH 7
INTELLECT 11
Deduction 14, linguistics 13, perception 13, trick 12
MIND 10
Artist: writer 13, cartography 11, research 12
CONFIDENCE 9
Con 11, willpower 10
CHARISMA 7
Persuasion 9

DERIVED ATTRIBUTES

9	**TOUGHNESS**
9	**TOUGHNESS** (w/armor)
5	**MRG** (Movement Rate, Ground)
3	**MRS** (Movement Rate, Swimming)
2	**MRC** (Movement Rate, Climbing)
2	**MRJ** (Movement Rate, Jumping)

LIFE POINTS 5	**SKILL POINTS**

COMBAT BOX   K   ○

WOUND LEVEL	**MODIFIERS**
○ *Light*	no modifier
○ *Moderate*	-2 to physical skills
○ *Heavy*	-4 physical & -2 all other skills
○ *Incapacitated*	-8 to all skills
○ *Mortal*	automatic KO; see text

SHOCK CAPACITY
SHOCK TAKEN

BACKGROUND

Advantages: Contacts (CI): several small-time researchers provide you with information you can use in your stories; Cultures (CI): as a child you spent a few years with your father traveling to several of Marl's cities, including Galitia, Selastos, and Padarr; Fame (CI): die-hard fans know you for your pulp tales; Luck (CII): see text on "Luck;" Learning Curve (CIII): Positive.

Compensations: Age (CI): you have just passed your 40th birthday; Poverty (CI): you must constantly pump out fiction to make ends meet; Quirk (CI): your right eye twitches involuntarily; Bigotry (CII): in your stories you always portray non-Humans as monsters; Quirk (CII): no matter when it happens, if you get an idea for a story, you have to drop everything else to write it down before you forget it; Achilles' Heel (CIII): you long to become a hero and therefore put yourself into any dangerous situation that arises.

DESCRIPTION

As a young boy you traveled to several of Marl's cities with your father, a researcher for any library or museum that would employ him. Everywhere you went you found interesting people, architecture, and ancient lore that you combined into exciting stories. Now, as a full-time novelist, you journey about the continent looking for anything that you can build into tales of high adventure.

EQUIPMENT

Journal; pens (7); fedora.

Tim Bobko

"I'm no Gibson Walters, but I get the job done."

BONUS CHART

DIE ROLL	2	3	4	5	6	7	8	9 10	11 12	13	14	15	16	17	18	19	20	21 26 25 30	31 35	36 40	41 45	+5
BONUS #	-10	-8	-7	-6	-5	-3	-1	0	1	2	3	4	5	6	7	8	9	10	11	12	13 14	+1

Bloodshadows™

GAMBLER

CHARACTER SHEET

SPECIES Human	ALIGNMENT Neutral	HEIGHT	MASS	AGE	SEX Male

ATTRIBUTES

AGILITY 6
Dodge 8, stealth 9, unarmed combat 7, unarmed parry 8
DEXTERITY 10
Prestidigitation 12
ENDURANCE 7
STRENGTH 6
INTELLECT 10
Deduction 12, perception 11, trick 12
MIND 8
CONFIDENCE 12
Alteration: vitomancy 13, con 13, gambling 14
CHARISMA 10

DERIVED ATTRIBUTES

8	**TOUGHNESS**
9	**TOUGHNESS** (w/armor)
4	**MRG** (Movement Rate, Ground)
3	**MRS** (Movement Rate, Swimming)
2	**MRC** (Movement Rate, Climbing)
2	**MRJ** (Movement Rate, Jumping)

LIFE POINTS 5	SKILL POINTS

COMBAT BOX   K   O

WOUND LEVEL	MODIFIERS
○ *Light*	no modifier
○ *Moderate*	-2 to physical skills
○ *Heavy*	-4 physical & -2 all other skills
○ *Incapacitated*	-8 to all skills
○ *Mortal*	automatic KO; see text

SHOCK CAPACITY
SHOCK TAKEN

BACKGROUND

Advantages: Additional Skill Adds (CI): +1 to gambling; Equipment (CI): deck of marked cards (adds +1 to *gambling* rolls); Wealth (CI): your parents owned a clothing shop, which you inherited and sold; Contacts (CII): you know streetsingers in several major cities who keep you informed of high-stakes gambling events; Luck (CIII): see text on "Luck."

Compensations: Enemy (CI): a gambling opponent believes you cheated him and wants revenge; Advantage Flaw (CI): once your inheritance runs out you will be destitute since you have no steady income; Quirk (CI): you constantly try to make bets on everything that happens around you; Cultural Unfamiliarity (CII): once someone catches you cheating, you head for the next town, which you usually know nothing about when you arrive; Learning Curve (CII): Negative; Bad Luck (CIII): see text on "Bad Luck."

DESCRIPTION

When your parents died in a fire at your home, you inherited their clothing store business. You didn't want to be constantly reminded of their deaths, so you sold off the store and moved out of Galitia. Soon you discovered the fun of gambling, especially since you had a great deal of money to start with, and began learning the "tricks" of the trade from those you met along the way. Your luck seems to run hot and cold — you either walk away with more than you can carry, or you end up broke.

Arcane Knowledges: Living Forces 1

Spells: *Facade*

EQUIPMENT

Marked deck of cards; .38 Gelvash revolver; extravagant clothing.

Tim Bobko

"There's nothing wrong with the cards. Just deal."

BONUS CHART

DIE ROLL	2	3	4	5	6	7	8	9 10	11 12	13	14	15	16	17	18	19	20	21 25	26 30	31 35	36 40	41 45	+5
BONUS #	-10	-8	-7	-6	-5	-3	-1	0	1	2	3	4	5	6	7	8	9	10	11	12	13	14	+1

Bloodshadows™

CHARACTER SHEET

TRADER

SPECIES Human	ALIGNMENT Order 1	HEIGHT	MASS	AGE	SEX Male

ATTRIBUTES

AGILITY 7
Dodge 9
DEXTERITY 6
Fire combat 8
ENDURANCE 8
STRENGTH 8
INTELLECT 10
Cantrips 11, deduction 11, perception 11, trick 12
MIND 8
Business 11
CONFIDENCE 13
Bribery 14, con 15, streetwise 14, will-power 11
CHARISMA 9
Charm 10, Persuasion 11

DERIVED ATTRIBUTES

9	**TOUGHNESS**
9	**TOUGHNESS** (w/armor)
5	**MRG** (Movement Rate, Ground)
4	**MRS** (Movement Rate, Swimming)
2	**MRC** (Movement Rate, Climbing)
2	**MRJ** (Movement Rate, Jumping)

LIFE POINTS	SKILL POINTS
5	

COMBAT BOX | K | ○

WOUND LEVEL | **MODIFIERS**

○ *Light* — no modifier
○ *Moderate* — -2 to physical skills
○ *Heavy* — -4 physical & -2 all other skills
○ *Incapacitated* — -8 to all skills
○ *Mortal* — automatic KO; see text

SHOCK CAPACITY	
SHOCK TAKEN	

BACKGROUND

Advantages: Additional Skill Adds (CI): +1 to con; Contacts (CI): you have a buyer in Padarr; Skill Bonus (CI): +1 to *con*, *charm*, and *persuasion* checks; Equipment (CII): Endel Truck; Additional Attribute Point (CIII): confidence.

Compensations: Advantage Flaw (CI): tied to Skill Bonus, you are stymied if you fail a *con*, *charm*, or *persuasion* check until the end of the scene or until you make a check successfully; Debt (CI): you owe your brother for the money he lent you to start your trading business; Quirk (CI): you are always worried that someone might steal your merchandise; Employment (CII): although you are technically self-employed, you have no other marketable skills that will earn you a living; Learning Curve (CII): Negative; Burn-out (CIII): you will lose your contacts if you are caught selling inferior merchandise to anyone.

DESCRIPTION

You've never really been good at anything, so you decided to go into the trading business. With a small loan you bought a truck and some merchandise and started transporting goods from suppliers to consumers. When times get rough, you sometimes offer your services to deliver "special" cargo — you don't ask what it is, and you're fairly certain you don't want to know.

Cantrips: *Awaken, candle, note*

EQUIPMENT

Endel truck; Degan "Guardian" rifle; handheld crystal set.

Tim Bobko

"It's a genuine copy of fake lassiter fur."

BONUS CHART

DIE ROLL	2	3	4	5	6	7	8	9 10	11 12	13	14	15	16	17	18	19	20	21 25	26 30	31 35	36 40	41 45	+5
BONUS #	-10	-8	-7	-6	-5	-3	-1	0	1	2	3	4	5	6	7	8	9	10	11	12	13	14	+1

Bloodshadows™

CHARACTER SHEET

DEMONLING

SPECIES Demonling	ALIGNMENT Chaos 1	HEIGHT	MASS	AGE	SEX Male

ATTRIBUTES

AGILITY 14
Climbing 16, long jumping 15, maneuver 15, stealth 15, unarmed combat 15
DEXTERITY 11
ENDURANCE 8
STRENGTH 10
INTELLECT 8
Perception 9, tracking 9, trick 9
MIND 6
CONFIDENCE 7
Intimidation 11, willpower 9
CHARISMA 5
Taunt 8

DERIVED ATTRIBUTES

10	**TOUGHNESS**
10	**TOUGHNESS** (w/armor)
8	**MRG** (Movement Rate, Ground)
5	**MRS** (Movement Rate, Swimming)
3	**MRC** (Movement Rate, Climbing)
3	**MRJ** (Movement Rate, Jumping)

LIFE POINTS 5	SKILL POINTS

COMBAT BOX   K   ○

WOUND LEVEL	MODIFIERS
○ *Light*	no modifier
○ *Moderate*	-2 to physical skills
○ *Heavy*	-4 physical & -2 all other skills
○ *Incapacitated*	-8 to all skills
○ *Mortal*	automatic KO; see text

SHOCK CAPACITY

SHOCK TAKEN

BACKGROUND

Advantages: Additional Skill Adds (CI): +1 to intimidation; Skill Bonus (CI): +1 to *climbing, long jumping, and maneuver* checks; Contacts (CI): you can always find a pack of Demonlings within two nights of searching; Luck (CII): see text on "Luck"; Additional Attribute Point (CIII): Agility.

Compensations: Cultural Unfamiliarity (CI): you feel awkward outside your pack; Prejudice (CI): most Humans consider your species inherently evil; Quirk (CI): you constantly sharpen your claws; Enemy (CII): sentinels or other defense forces tend to chase you away whenever they discover you in their midst; Learning Curve (CII): Negative; Achilles' Heel (CIII): if you spend more than one month away from your pack, you lose your contacts with them permanently.

DESCRIPTION

Everyone considers you the lowest of the demonic species, but you beg to differ. You sow just as much chaos — more, even — than many of your kin, though you tend to do so through less grandiose methods. You have no need of arcane abilities, for your brute strength and quick reflexes provide you with all the power you require to work your mischief. Usually you wander with packs of demonlings, hunting and killing whatever crosses your path, though sometimes you need to part with them to restore your sense of individuality.

Natural Tools: Claws, damage value STR+4/15; teeth, damage value STR+3/14

Tim Bobko

"Stop being funny so I can spit."

BONUS CHART

								9	11											21	26	31	36	41	
DIE ROLL	2	3	4	5	6	7	8	10	12	13	14	15	16	17	18	19	20	25	30	35	40	45	+5
BONUS #	-10	-8	-7	-6	-5	-3	-1	0	1	2	3	4	5	6	7	8	9	10	11	12	13	14	+1